CW00919247

LIBREX

MACMILLAN

MACMILLAN READERS

INTERMEDIATE LEVEL

Founding Editor: John Milne

The Macmillan Readers provide a choice of enjoyable reading materials for learners of English. The series is published at six levels – Starter, Beginner, Elementary, Pre-Intermediate, Intermediate and Upper.

Level control
Information, structure and vocabulary are controlled to suit the students' ability at each level.

The number of words at each level:

Starter	about 300 basic words
Beginner	about 600 basic words
Elementary	about 1100 basic words
Pre-Intermediate	about 1400 basic words
Intermediate	about 1600 basic words
Upper	about 2200 basic words

Vocabulary
Some difficult words and phrases in this book are important for understanding the story. Some of these words are explained in the story and some are shown in the pictures. From Pre-Intermediate level upwards, words are marked with a number like this: ...³. These words are explained in the Glossary at the end of the book.

Contents

A Note About the Author

Wilbur Addison Smith was born on 9th January, 1933 in the southern African country which is now called Zambia. At that time, the country was called Northern Rhodesia. It was governed by the British and many British people lived there. Wilbur Smith was educated in South Africa, where he lived for many years.

Wilbur Smith's first book – *When the Lion Feeds* – was published in 1964. Since then Wilbur Smith has written more than twenty-eight novels. His work has been translated into twenty-five languages. All of the novels are adventure stories and many of them take place in Africa. Although some of Wilbur Smith's novels are set in the late twentieth century, most of them are historical novels. The author has written several series of novels about the adventures of families over a long period of time.

Wilbur Smith publishes a new novel every two years, and several of his books have been made into successful films.

The Seventh Scroll is a modern thriller that is set in the late twentieth century. But it is a sequel[1] to an earlier book called *River God*, which is a historical novel set in Ancient Egypt, nearly 4000 years ago. A retelling of *River God* is also available in this series of Readers, although it is not necessary to read it before you read *The Seventh Scroll*. *River God* is set at the time when Egypt was invaded[2] by people from western Asia, who the Egyptians called the Hyksos. In the story, *The Seventh Scroll*, some Ancient Egyptian records are discovered. They had been written on scrolls of papyrus[3] and one of them told of a tomb that had been built for an Egyptian king at the time of the Hyksos invasion.

The People in This Story

Duraid and Royan Al Simma

Nicholas Quenton-Harper

Nahoot Gudabbi

Geoffrey Tenant

Gotthold von Schiller

Boris Brusilov

Woizero Tessay

Mek Nimmur

Colonel Nogo

Sapper Webb and Jannie

1

Death by the Nile

Doctor Duraid Al Simma was sitting on a chair in the garden of his villa. His wife, Doctor Royan Al Simma, was sitting beside him. It was late in the afternoon and the sun was sinking low in the sky.

The house was not far from the city of Cairo, the capital city of Egypt. There were palm trees on three sides of the area of land where the villa stood. On the fourth side, the River Nile flowed.

Duraid and Royan Al Simma were Egyptologists. They studied the ancient monuments[4] of their country and they studied its history. They both worked at the Department of Antiquities[5] in Cairo.

Royan was much younger than her husband. She was thirty-two years old. Her father had been Egyptian but her mother had been English. Royan had a British passport. She and her husband both wrote and spoke English as well as Arabic.

The two of them were eating a simple meal of dates, olives and flat bread. Royan looked across the river at the setting sun. As the red sun sank behind the palm trees on the west bank of the river, it coloured the water red. The water from the River Nile kept a narrow strip of Egypt green and alive. Beyond the trees, lay the brown, dry desert where few things could live.

The air became cool as the sun set. Soon, night had fallen and stars were shining brightly in the dark sky. The noises of crickets and frogs came from the river, together with the gentle sound of the flowing water.

Duraid stood up and went into the villa through the back door. He turned on the lights in the villa, then he called to his wife. 'Well, it's time to start work,' he said.

Royan went into the main room of the house – the living room. As usual, the living room looked like a library. There were books and papers everywhere. There were piles of books on shelves and piles of papers on the floor. All of the books and papers were about Ancient Egypt.

In the corner of the room was a steel safe. Royan opened the heavy door of the safe and took out a scroll made of papyrus. It was very old.

'The Seventh Scroll,' Royan said to herself.

This scroll was almost 4000 years old and she loved to hold it and read it. The words on the scroll were written in hieroglyphics[6]. This was the written language which the Egyptian people used for thousands of years before they wrote and spoke Arabic.

The man who had written the scroll was a slave[7] called Taita. He had lived at the time of the Hyksos invasion of Egypt, nearly 4000 years ago.

Taita was the slave of Lostris, a Queen of Egypt. When the Hyksos invaded the land, Lostris had led her people to the south to escape the invaders. She had led them into the land of Cush – the area which now forms the countries of Sudan and Ethiopia.

Somewhere, in Ethiopia, these exile[8] Egyptians had built a tomb for their dead king – the Pharaoh Mamose – Lostris's husband. Later the exiles had returned to Egypt. Taita had written about the life of Lostris, soon after her death. He had written this record on ten scrolls. The scrolls had been found in Lostris's own tomb, which had recently been discovered. In the Seventh Scroll, Taita had described the building of Mamose's tomb. But the slave did not describe the place exactly, because he did not want anyone to find it. He had done his work well – the location of the tomb was still a secret!

Now Royan and her husband wanted to find that tomb.

They believed that it was somewhere in the Ethiopian mountains, but they did not have any proof of this. They only had the writings of Taita. Very few Egyptologists believed that the tomb really existed.

'Taita says that the tomb is at the second "step" of the river,' said Duraid. 'We have looked at many maps, we have looked at satellite photographs[9], and we are still not sure which river he meant.'

'We have talked about this many times already,' said Royan. 'Taita was proud of the tomb. He designed it himself. His workmen spent fifteen years building it – that's what the scroll says. He wanted us to know about it, but he didn't want us to *find* it. He hid it very well.'

'Someone will have to look for it,' Duraid told her. 'First we must finish the translation of the Seventh Scroll and then we must guess where to look in Ethiopia.'

'We know that Taita and the Egyptian exiles travelled east from Cush – the country now called Sudan,' his wife said. 'They went along the Blue Nile. Taita described this river as "the dark river", and we guess that he did not build the tomb close beside the Nile itself. In the Seventh Scroll, Taita writes about mountains and a second "step" – which probably means a cataract or a waterfall. We must find a place where the river water flows quickly over rocks. This area may be difficult to reach, but a lot of people had to live there while they built the tomb. Perhaps people still live near there.'

'Yes, I agree,' Duraid answered. 'Let us believe that Taita wrote about another river that flows *into* the Blue Nile,' Duraid pointed at a map. 'The most likely place is here on the Dandera River. There is a large monastery[10] near the place now. People have lived there for hundreds of years, so it must be possible to grow food there. The people who live there now will know if there are hidden caves or other secret

'He wanted us to know about it, but he didn't want us to find it.'

places. Also, there will be signs of the work on ancient build-ings. Even after 4000 years, we'll find the marks the Ancient Egyptians left. They built the Pharaoh's tomb with stone. They had to cut the stone from somewhere. We must look for a quarry or a mine where they dug the stone out of the ground.'

'This always brings us back to the problem of money,' said Royan. 'We need an expedition[11] to search for the tomb. That means hiring[12] a lot of men and equipment. And that will cost a lot of money. Who will pay for this expedition?'

'American museums have the most money to spend on Egyptology,' Duraid answered. 'They will certainly buy ancient objects, but they will not pay for expeditions that might fail. We have so little proof to show them.'

'You said that an Austrian was interested.'

'Yes, Gotthold von Schiller. He asked our colleague, Nahoot Gudabbi, about the scrolls. I know that von Schiller owns objects from many tombs. He buys them on the black market[13]. I don't like the man and I don't trust him!'

'Who else is there?' asked Royan.

'There is an English collector[14] called Nicholas Quenton-Harper,' Duraid replied. 'Do you remember him? He was a friend of your father, and I've met him several times. He once travelled to Ethiopia and sailed a boat along the Blue Nile. I think we should ask him first.'

'Nicholas Quenton-Harper. Yes, you're right – he might be interested. He *is* a collector and he's a very rich man. So, how do we contact him?'

'I'll write to Mr Quenton-Harper — ' Duraid stopped speaking. There was the noise of dogs barking near the house. 'Someone is outside,' he said, 'I'll find out who it is.' He picked up an oil lamp and lit it.

'Be careful,' said Royan. The nearest village was a kilometre away and the Egyptologists did not receive many visitors at their villa.

The front door of the villa led directly into the living room where they had been talking. Duraid Al Simma opened the door and looked outside. Royan looked over his shoulder. Suddenly, she saw a man come out of the darkness. His face was covered with a scarf, and he held a knife in his hand. He stabbed the knife into Duraid Al Simma's chest.

The oil lamp fell from Duraid's hand. It broke and set fire to some of the papers on the floor. Immediately, bright flames began to burn across the room. Duraid only had time to say 'Run!' to Royan, then he fell down.

Royan saw two more men appear outside the front door. She ran out of the back door of the house and into the garden.

'Leave her!' she heard one man shout to the other. 'Get the papers!'

Royan ran down to the river and hid in the tall reeds that grew by the water. A few minutes later, the men came to search for her. She was sure that they wanted to kill her, but she did not know why.

The whole house was on fire now, and it was burning very quickly. The men did not search for very long. After a few more minutes, Royan heard a car drive away.

———

People from the nearest village saw the fire and they came to help. The police came as well. But none of them could save the house and they could not help Doctor Duraid Al Simma. Royan's husband was dead.

2

A Visit to England

Royan spent that night in a hospital, although she was not hurt. She had many visitors. Friends and relatives came to see her as soon as they heard what had happened.

'You must stay with us,' they all said. 'This is a terrible thing to happen. And your house is destroyed.'

'Thank you,' Royan said to everyone, 'but I want to be alone. I still have our apartment in Cairo. Duraid and I were happy there. We did a lot of our work together in that apartment. I want to stay there on my own now and remember him.'

The last visitor was Nahoot Gudabbi. He was a tall thin man with dark eyes. He was a colleague. He also worked at the Department of Antiquities. But Royan did not like him.

'What happened to all your papers?' Nahoot asked. 'You were working on an important scroll.'

'Everything was burnt or stolen,' said Royan. 'The scroll and all our papers are gone.'

'And do you have copies?'

'Yes, fortunately I do have copies,' Royan answered. 'We photographed everything, including the Seventh Scroll itself. We kept copies of all our notes. They are in our apartment in Cairo. I will take them to the Egyptian Museum tomorrow for safety.'

'Ah, good, good,' said Nahoot Gudabbi. He had an unpleasant way of speaking. 'They will be very safe there, I am sure of that.'

Royan was pleased when he left. She wanted to escape from all the people who wanted to help her. She wanted to get back to her work. She wanted to finish her dead husband's translation of the Seventh Scroll.

When she left the hospital, she took a taxi to the apartment which was her home in the city. She walked slowly up the stairs and stopped outside her door. Something was wrong – the door of her apartment was open. She saw that someone had broken in. Inside her apartment there was a terrible mess – all her books and clothes were on the floor.

She went into the study. She had kept all her notes and photographs in a filing cabinet there. The cabinet was empty! The drawers had been broken open. All the notes and computer disks had been taken from her desk drawer. The computer lay on the floor, broken into several pieces. All of the Al Simmas' work had gone.

Royan wanted to go too. She felt angry and upset. So much had gone wrong in such a short time. She wanted to get away from all this, but where could she go?

She tidied up the apartment a little. When she felt better, she packed a case. Then she took a taxi to her bank and asked to talk to a clerk.

'I want to take everything from my safety deposit box[15],' she told the man.

'We normally expect notice of withdrawal[16],' said the bank clerk.

Royan pretended that she did not understand. She was a good-looking woman and she smiled at the clerk. The clerk smiled at her, and a few minutes later she had the box. It contained her British passport and several hundred pounds – more than enough money to buy a plane ticket to London.

Royan was thinking about her husband's last words. She wanted to find Nicholas Quenton-Harper.

————

Nicholas Quenton-Harper lived in a large old house called Quenton Park. Royan found Nicholas Quenton-Harper's name and his address in the telephone directory[17]. She phoned the house and spoke to a secretary. Royan explained

13

who she was and arranged to visit immediately.

The house was surrounded by tall trees and it had a large extension[18] at the back. This extension was a museum. Nicholas Quenton-Harper's great-grandfather had started the museum in 1885. He had collected many Egyptian antiquities. The family had added to the collection for over a century since then. The Quenton-Harpers had been soldiers and diplomats[19] and explorers. They had travelled all over the world and they had collected many rare and valuable objects. The museum now contained one of the best private collections of Egyptian antiquities.

Nicholas Quenton-Harper was about forty years old. There were many silver-grey hairs on his head, but he had a young face and a pleasant smile.

'I am Royan Al Simma,' Royan told him as they shook hands. 'I believe that you knew my father and my husband, Duraid Al Simma.'

'Yes, that's right,' said Quenton-Harper. 'I was sorry to learn about your husband's death. I do hope that you were not harmed in the attack.'

'Thank you for your kind words. I wasn't hurt. And I am trying to carry on my husband's work,' said Royan. 'May I tell you a story?'

'Of course you may,' said Nicholas Quenton-Harper. 'But first, may I show you the museum?'

Royan enjoyed her tour of the museum. She saw that many of the objects had come from Egypt. Collectors had been taking ancient artefacts out of Egypt for centuries. Sometimes they bought them. Sometimes they just took them. The British had taken more than anyone else.

She examined a tall statue of a man who wore sandals and a short kilt[20]. He carried a war bow[21] in his hand.

'There is a statue exactly like this in the Egyptian Museum,' said Royan.

14

'I am trying to carry on my husband's work,' said Royan.

'Yes, they are a pair,' said Nicholas. 'Can you read the inscription?'

Royan looked at the hieroglyphics on the base of the statue and read aloud – 'I am Ramses, Lord of Ten Thousand Chariots.'

'You're a good scholar,' said Nicholas. 'Which period of Egyptian history do you like most?'

'I'm most interested in the Hyksos period,' Royan replied. 'My husband and I found scrolls that described a tomb in Ethiopia. It was built when Queen Lostris took her people south from Egypt to escape from the Hyksos.'

'I've heard stories about the secret tomb of Pharaoh Mamose,' said Nicholas, 'but I don't believe them. Can you show me these scrolls?'

'Nine of the ten scrolls are in Egypt,' said Royan. 'The Seventh Scroll, which describes the tomb, was stolen together with all our notes and photographs. My husband was murdered for it.'

'Oh, I'm sorry,' said the Englishman. 'We won't talk about it any more.'

'But I *want* to talk about it,' said Royan. 'I want your help to find the secret tomb of Pharaoh Mamose. I believe it is somewhere on the Dandera River in Ethiopia. I also understand that you once sailed down the Blue Nile.'

'Well, I sailed down a part of the Blue Nile. I've also been to the Dandera Valley. But you say that you've lost all your notes and the scroll. How will you find the tomb?'

Royan looked at Quenton-Harper. 'I have a very good memory,' she said quietly. 'And I want to find the tomb before the murderers of my husband get there. Someone else believes that the tomb is in Ethiopia. That person killed my husband for the information. That is the only proof I have. Will you help me Mr Quenton-Harper?'

Quenton-Harper looked surprised for a moment, then he smiled. 'I'd like that very much. I haven't been to Ethiopia

16

for at least a dozen years. Yes, I'll certainly help you. Please call me Nicholas. May I call you Royan?'

———

Nicholas made all the arrangements. He booked their flights to Addis Ababa. He hired a guide who would take them to the Dandera River. He invented a false story to tell his friends. He told them that he and Royan were going to hunt animals in Ethiopia.

Nicholas and Royan stayed in Addis Ababa for a few days. Nicholas wanted to see a friend who worked at the British Embassy – a man called Geoffrey Tenant.

'We're going on an expedition into the mountains,' said Nicholas. 'We want to do some hunting along the Dandera River.'

'Be very careful,' said Geoffrey. 'There are rebel soldiers along the Blue Nile near the border with Sudan. They are fighting against government soldiers. The rebels rob tourists when they find them. That's why the country doesn't get many visitors.'

'We won't take any risks[22],' said Nicholas. 'I've hired a guide – a Russian called Boris Brusilov.'

'I've heard of him,' said Geoffrey. Suddenly he looked very worried. 'I've heard of him, but I haven't heard anything good about him.'

The next day, Nicholas and Royan flew in a small plane to Lake Tana. The country was mountainous and green. It was Royan's first visit to this part of Africa and she thought that the landscape was beautiful and exciting.

Two guides were waiting for them at Lake Tana. A tall African woman walked to their plane as soon as it landed.

'My name is Woizero Tessay,' she told them. 'My husband is Boris Brusilov. We will be your guides.'

Boris was dressed in a cream-coloured suit. He had very pale blue eyes. 'Where do you want to go?' he asked.

17

'We're interested in doing some hunting,' Nicholas replied. 'Also I want to see the old Monastery of St Frumentius on the Dandera River. I'm writing an article for a geographical magazine. I don't think anyone has written about that place before. Will you take us there?'

'We'll go wherever you want. You're paying for the trip,' said Boris. 'I know the Monastery of St Frumentius. Not many travellers go there because it's difficult to reach. I took some men from a mining company there recently. Pegasus Mining was the name of their company. Do you know it?'

'No, I don't,' said Nicholas, but he decided to ask Geoffrey Tenant about the company. Geoffrey would know about the people from Pegasus and what they wanted in the Dandera River Valley. What minerals could they be looking for there?

Tessay and Boris helped Nicholas and Royan carry their equipment from the plane to a four-wheel-drive truck.

3

The Monastery of St Frumentius

The roads were bad and the truck bumped and shook as it drove over the rough ground. Hour after hour, Royan stared out of the window at the landscape. Slowly the landscape changed from green to brown and then to grey – the colour of the rocks. There were many strange trees and birds but there were very few people near the road.

Each night they all camped in tents. Boris put up the tents and Tessay cooked the food. Then Boris got a bottle of vodka out of his luggage and drank the strong drink until he fell asleep. Royan saw that Tessay was afraid of her husband when he was drunk.

On the third evening, the travellers reached the cliffs above the Dandera River.

'We'll leave the truck here,' said Boris. 'We must walk from this point. I will hire men to carry the equipment.'

Royan looked over the edge of the cliffs. 'We'll walk? Do you mean that we have to climb straight down there?' she said in horror.

'No,' Boris answered, 'we won't climb – there is a long path that goes to the river at the bottom. So tomorrow, we walk. Now, I need a drink.'

——

The next day, they left the truck and began walking on the path down the cliff. Some men from a nearby village carried the equipment. These men knew the path, which was narrow but not difficult to walk on. Royan did not like the idea that they would have to ascend the cliffs again.

It was a long descent. When she passed the places where there was a sheer drop[23] on one side of the path, she did not look down.

'You can't see the Blue Nile from here,' said Boris, 'because the cliffs hide the view. But soon you'll see the Dandera River. It's in that valley over there.' He pointed with his finger towards the south.

'I see that there are *two* valleys,' said Nicholas. 'Perhaps the river has changed its course over the years.'

'Yes, perhaps it has,' agreed Boris. 'I've never thought of that. There are many dry valleys here, but they fill with water for a few weeks in the rainy season.'

'The river has probably changed its course since Taita was alive,' said Royan. 'Taita said that the tomb was near the second step of the river.'

'The tomb? What tomb?' asked Boris.

'Oh, the tomb of Frumentius,' Nicholas answered quickly. 'The monastery has a famous tomb, doesn't it?'

'Yes, it does,' said Boris. 'Many pilgrims come to pray at the monastery. But they never see the tomb itself. Only the priests can go into the tomb.'

'OK, but we can visit the monastery, can't we?' asked Royan.

'That's no problem,' answered Boris. 'Many people will visit it this week. There's a special festival there called Timkat. In fact, I thought that that was why you had come – to see the festival. It's very interesting.'

'Yes,' said Nicholas quickly, 'I do want to take photos of the festival of Timkat.'

'That is something that you can do,' said Boris. 'But you *can't* see the tomb of Frumentius.'

———

The air became hotter as the travellers descended into the valley. They made their camp at the bottom of the cliffs beside the Dandera River. Night was falling by the time they had set up their tents.

'Listen. Can you hear singing?' Royan asked.

A few minutes later, a group of priests came along the river bank. They were dressed in white robes, they held burning torches in their hands and they were singing. Four young priests carried an old man in a chair. The old man had a long silver-grey beard.

'That is the abbot of the St Frumentius Monastery,' said Boris. 'He is more than one hundred years old.'

The priests halted[24]. They stopped singing and they stood around the abbot. The old man spoke Amharic in a high voice.

'He's saying kind words about you,' said Boris. 'Now you'll be welcome at the monastery.'

Nicholas thanked the abbot. Tessay translated between English and Amharic. The abbot replied and Tessay told Nicholas what he had said.

20

'The abbot welcomes you and invites you to eat a meal at the monastery tomorrow night.'

Then the priests left. They sang as they returned to the monastery. The light of their torches and the sound of their singing disappeared slowly into the night.

———

The next morning Nicholas and Royan explored the valley. Several smaller streams of water ran beside the Dandera River. There were also two channels that looked like dry river beds.

'I think that the Dandera *has* changed its course over the centuries,' said Nicholas. 'Look at these channels. The river has not always run along its present course.'

'Do you think that the course was very different in Taita's time?' asked Royan. She looked at the high cliffs on either side of the valley. 'There are so many places where a tomb could be hidden.'

'Yes, there are,' Nicholas agreed. 'Now, let's go and look at the monastery.'

The buildings of the Monastery of St Frumentius were cut into a cliff of rock. People had lived here for over a thousand years. They grew crops in narrow strips of land by the Nile. They caught fish from the river. The priests themselves had cut many tunnels and chambers[25] and steps into the rock, but there were also some natural caves. The main part of the monastery – its church – was in one of these huge caves. It was lit by oil lamps. There were carvings and paintings on the walls.

Nicholas and Royan went through the heavy outer doors into the church and joined a crowd of people. The crowd filled the first, main part of the church. The people were praying and singing while many priests moved among them. The smell of burning incense[26] and the smell of burning oil lamps was strong. It made the air difficult to breathe.

At the far end of the church was a pair of wooden doors. Priests stood in front of them.

'I expect they're guarding the tomb,' said Nicholas. 'The tomb of St Frumentius is probably beyond those wooden doors. We'll find out later, when we come here to dinner.'

Nicholas and Royan went back to their camp and rested for a while. At sunset they returned to the monastery. A group of priests welcomed them and took them back to the church in the cave. A table and seats had been put in there. The first, main part was now a dining hall. Royan and Nicholas sat near the abbot while priests filled the rest of the hall.

Large plates of food were brought from the kitchens. These plates were covered with a thin bread called *injera*. There were also bowls of hot meat and gravy.

The old abbot was enjoying himself. He was wearing brightly coloured robes. On his head he wore a crown with a blue stone in the centre. He ate bread and meat and he drank a strong liquid called *tej*. He offered some of this drink to Nicholas and Royan.

'I'm sure that Boris would like this,' said Nicholas. He was enjoying the *tej*, but it made Royan cough.

Nicholas watched the wooden doors at the end of the church. The guards there never left their places. They sat and ate in front of the doors.

'The tomb of St Frumentius is there?' he asked the abbot, pointing at the doors.

The old man nodded his head.

Royan was watching the abbot carefully. She was not enjoying the food or the drink, but she was very interested in the abbot's crown.

'Do you see anything unusual about that crown?' she asked Nicholas quietly.

'No, I don't think so,' he replied. 'It's made of brass, not

On his head he wore a crown with a blue stone in the centre.

gold, and the jewels are made of glass.'

'But look at the blue stone in the centre. It has an inscription on it. Can you read it?'

At the end of the meal, Nicholas thanked the abbot for the meal. While he was talking to the old man, he looked closely at the blue stone in the crown. The inscription was not in Amharic, it was written in Egyptian hieroglyphics. The stone was very old.

As they left the monastery, Nicholas told Royan about the unusual inscription. 'I was able to read it,' he said. 'It means, "I am Lord of Ten Thousand Chariots. I am Taita the master of the royal horses." It was quite clear.'

'So, we were right, Taita *was* here,' Royan said excitedly. 'We'll find the royal tomb here, I *know* that we will! But where shall we start looking?'

'Let's begin with the tomb of Frumentius,' Nicholas said. 'We'll have to think of a way to get past the guards. Now, let's get some sleep.'

They went back to their tents. Nicholas lay in his tent and thought about the tomb of Frumentius. He thought about how to get past the guards. Just before he fell asleep, he had an idea.

4

A Friend From the Past

Something woke Nicholas suddenly. It was the cold metal barrel of a gun which was pressing against his head. The night was still dark and he could not see who was holding the gun.

'Who are you? What do you want?' he asked angrily.

Then he heard the voice of Tessay outside the tent.

'Be careful, Nicholas,' said Tessay. 'We're surrounded by rebel soldiers. They want us to go with them.'

Nicholas came out of his tent and looked around. The soldiers were wearing camouflage uniforms[27]. Nicholas could not see the men clearly, but he could see the metal of their guns shining in the moonlight. He joined Royan and Tessay who were standing together.

'Where's Boris?' he asked.

'Boris is drunk. We can't wake him.'

The rebel soldiers left Boris in his tent. They led Nicholas and Royan and Tessay along the bank of the Dandera River. They walked upstream[28], away from the monastery. They kept moving until they reached a camp below a cliff. There was a waterfall nearby which made a loud noise as it splashed onto the rocks.

A man was sitting at a table in the middle of the camp. He was studying a map by the light of an oil lamp. He looked up. He was a good-looking man with a charming smile.

'Nicholas Quenton-Harper,' he said happily. 'I'm happy to see you again.'

'Mek Nimmur,' said Nicholas, 'are we your guests or your prisoners?'

'You are our guests, of course, but I couldn't invite you here openly[29],' the man answered. 'You know that I am not a supporter of the present government. There could be problems for you if you accepted an invitation from me, so I forced you to come. I hope that you aren't too unhappy about that.'

'Mek and I are friends,' Nicholas explained to Royan and Tessay. 'Mek helped me when I came here before. He pulled me out of the river when my boat sank.'

'Who are your companions?' Mek Nimmur asked. He looked at Tessay and smiled. 'And why are you here?'

'Mek Nimmur, are we your guests or your prisoners?'

'I've come here to photograph the Monastery of St Frumentius,' said Nicholas. 'These ladies are helping me.'

'You're a bad liar, Nicholas,' said Mek Nimmur, laughing. 'But don't answer my question if you don't want to. You know that I'm always ready to help you. My men and I are going to the monastery this evening for the festival of Timkat.'

'Do you use the monastery as a base?' asked Nicholas.

Mek Nimmur smiled but did not answer the question. 'Tonight is the festival of Timkat,' he said. 'Everyone will go to the river to celebrate. You must come too.'

Then he spoke to Tessay. 'I knew your father. Is it true that you now live with a drunken Russian?'

Tessay looked at the ground. She said nothing. Nicholas guessed that she did not want to go back to Boris.

———

Later, when Nicholas and Royan returned to their own camp, Tessay stayed with Mek Nimmur.

'Everyone will go down to the river tonight,' Nicholas said to Royan. 'The monastery will be empty. And we'll go to the tomb of St Frumentius tonight.'

'But what if someone sees us?' asked Royan.

'We must make sure that nobody sees us,' Nicholas replied.

They rested for a few hours at their own camp. Then, in the afternoon, they made preparations to get into the monastery. Nicholas had two cameras. He wanted to photograph everything that they found in the tomb.

Boris interrupted their preparations. 'Where is Tessay?' he asked angrily. He had been drinking vodka again. He stared drunkenly at Nicholas and Royan. Both of them were silent.

'I will find her,' he said and he walked away towards the monastery.

Nicholas did not try to stop him. Mek Nimmur could look after himself. And he could also look after Tessay.

———

27

That evening, Nicholas and Royan went to the monastery at sunset. They saw all the priests and many of the people from the village going down to the river. The priests held burning torches in their hands. They sang as they led the people to the river.

The old abbot came out of the monastery. Two young priests helped him to walk to the river. He was wearing magnificent robes and a different crown. He followed the people down to the river.

Nicholas saw Tessay in the crowd. She was with Mek Nimmur. Boris was in the crowd as well.

'We must go into the monastery church while there are still a few people inside,' said Nicholas. 'When everyone has left the church and gone to the river, we can look at the tomb.'

They went into the big church. There were huge curtains hanging along one wall. Nicholas and Royan hid behind a curtain and they waited. The guards of the tomb were the last people to leave the church. They closed the heavy outer doors of the church behind them. Now Nicholas and Royan were alone in the building.

'They've locked the doors at the entrance,' said Nicholas. 'That's good.'

'Yes. At least we won't be disturbed,' Royan agreed.

Nicholas was carrying a camera bag. He opened it and took out a torch. 'It has new batteries,' he said, handing it to Royan. 'But don't waste them. We may be here all night.'

The wooden doors of the tomb were decorated with pictures. They showed scenes from the life of St Frumentius. They showed how the holy man had arrived from Byzantium[30] and founded the monastery.

The doors to the tomb had a simple lock. Nicholas turned the lock easily and opened one of the doors. They stepped inside the tomb and closed the door behind them. Royan shone her torch on the walls.

28

They were in a small room with a low ceiling. There were shelves around the walls. On the shelves were small statues, paintings, metal pots and bowls, jewelled boxes and candle sticks. Pilgrims brought these gifts to the tomb. Many of the objects were hundreds of years old.

Nicholas and Royan moved slowly to the back of the room. They saw an entrance to another room. Royan shone her torch inside and called out.

'Nicholas, look! This is the inner tomb! It's much, much older than the rest of the building – and it's Egyptian!'

A coffin lay on a stone shelf at the back of the tomb. There was a picture of a man's face painted on the lid of the coffin. Although the colours were faded, they could see that the pale face of this man had a short red beard. It was a proud, noble face.

There was an inscription on the shelf below the coffin. Royan read the ancient hieroglyphics. 'This is the sign of Tanus, Lord Harrab,' she said. 'The Great Lion of Egypt. The best of One Hundred Thousand. Companion of Pharaoh. Warrior of the Gods.'

'This is Taita's work,' said Royan. 'Look around. We need to find the sarcophagus[31] of Pharaoh Mamose. Can you find any clues?'

'We must photograph everything here and study the pictures later,' said Nicholas. 'We won't get another chance to examine this tomb.'

'Here is another inscription,' said Royan. She looked closely at a stone pillar. She read her translation to Nicholas.

The lesser place is for the highest.
The greater place is lowest,
Covered over at the second step.
May Hapi guard it for all time.

'Do these words mean anything to you?' asked Nicholas.

'Hapi was the Egyptian god of the River Nile,' answered

Royan. 'Taita wrote about the second step in the Seventh Scroll. Duraid and I *thought* that it meant a cataract or waterfall. The second tomb must be at the second step of the river.'

'So we ought to look near a waterfall,' said Nicholas.

'Or behind or below a waterfall,' agreed Royan.

'Do you mean that the tomb could be under the river?'

'We don't know. We'll have to search carefully. Remember, you said that the course of the river might have changed. We might not find a waterfall in the same place that Taita did.'

They photographed everything in the tomb. It took them half the night. When they left the tomb, they closed the wooden doors behind them and looked for a way out of the church.

'The priests don't use the main entrance much,' Nicholas said. 'We must look for a different way to their living quarters.'

They soon found a small door behind a curtain. Through the door there was a passage that led to the priests' rooms. At the end of the passage, a door opened to the outside. They saw the river and the path which led back to their camp. They went back to their tents and slept until midday.

———

Boris woke up everyone in the camp.

'She's gone!' he shouted. 'Tessay has left with a rebel soldier. I'll kill both of them!'

'That's not our problem,' said Nicholas. 'Now let me sleep.'

'I'll find them. I'll kill them!' shouted Boris. 'You helped her. I'll make trouble for you too!'

He picked up a gun and walked away along the river bank.

'Shall we follow him?' asked Royan. 'Will Tessay be safe?'

'Mek Nimmur can take care of himself,' said Nicholas. 'And he'll take care of Tessay. But I want to go back to Mek's camp. He won't be there. I want to look at that waterfall near his camp. Do you remember it?'

5

The Quarry

Royan and Nicholas went upstream to the site of Mek Nimmur's camp. There was no sign of Mek and there was no sign of his camp. There were no marks or objects left on the ground. Mek had covered his tracks well. Boris would not follow him easily.

Nicholas and Royan looked at the waterfall. A great spout of water rushed through a gap in the rocks above them. It fell noisily into a wide pool. The water from the pool flowed quietly down two broad stone steps.

'You said that Taita wrote about *the second step*,' said Nicholas. But could the words mean the *two steps*?'

'It's possible to translate the words that way,' said Royan. 'Ancient Egyptian is not clear about numbers and plurals. We have to guess a little when we translate.'

'That pool is deep,' said Nicholas. 'We will need diving equipment[32] to find out what's down there.'

'The Ancient Egyptians didn't have diving equipment,' Royan said thoughtfully. 'They could build pyramids and tombs, but they couldn't work under water.'

'Maybe the water in the river was lower then,' said Nicholas. 'Maybe there were dry seasons. Maybe the Dandera—' He stopped in the middle of his sentence. Then he went on, 'Well, let's look up, instead of down.'

'Where do you mean?' asked Royan.

'Let's look up above the water spout,' said Nicholas. 'Let's climb up to the top of the waterfall and have a look there.'

It took them a quarter of an hour to reach the top of the waterfall. They had to climb a track that led up a steep hill. At the top, the river was only about twelve metres wide, but the water moved very swiftly[33] as it flowed towards the spout.

31

Nicholas walked along the river bank. He looked carefully at the rocks along the edge of the river.

'What are you looking for?' asked Royan.

'Excavations. Marks cut into the stone by metal tools. Anything that shows digging or mining.'

'But, would there be any marks of ancient excavations after all these years?'

'Probably not,' said Nicholas. 'The water has worn the river banks away over the years. But still, I want to check. There may be signs of excavation further along the river.'

'But aren't we moving away from the site of the tomb?' asked Royan. 'If we are right, and if the tomb is somewhere near this waterfall, shouldn't we look downstream? Did the Ancient Egyptians dig the pool and those steps?'

'It's possible, but I think that those steps are natural,' said Nicholas. 'I don't think that the Egyptians cut them from the rock. What I'm looking for is the digging that happened *before* Lostris's people built the tomb.'

'What did they build first?'

'I think they built a dam[34] to change the course of the river.'

'Could they do that?'

'Well, the Ancient Egyptians could build canals and dams. They worked mainly with earth and mud bricks, but they knew how to work with stone. They built pyramids from huge blocks of stone. And remember that the Pyramids at Giza were built without the use of wheels or hard metal – and that was a thousand years before Taita's time. I believe that he and his men could have built a dam. In fact, I believe that they could have built it right *there*.'

As he spoke, Nicholas pointed with his finger towards a place where the river was narrower – not more than ten metres wide. On one side of the river, there was a channel that looked smoother than the surrounding rocks.

'I guess that the river once ran down there,' said Nicholas, pointing to the channel. 'The water must have worn the sides of the channel smooth. Let's look a little further.'

Royan and Nicholas had to clamber[35] over large rocks at the side of the river. High walls of rock rose on either side of them and made dark shadows on the swiftly flowing water.

'We'd better go back to our camp. It'll be sunset soon,' said Royan.

'Let's go a little further,' said Nicholas.

A minute later, they found an opening in the rock wall and went through it to a large area that was the shape of a bowl. The walls of the bowl were steep and straight. But there were also places where steps had been cut into the rock walls.

'This was once a quarry,' said Nicholas. 'Stone masons used simple metal tools to make holes in the top of these rocks. Then they hammered pieces of wood into the holes until the rocks broke. And, as you see, they knew how to break the rocks into square blocks.'

There were several blocks of stone on the floor of the quarry. The blocks had smooth sides. They had been waiting for someone to move them for thirty-eight centuries.

'And what did Taita's people do with these blocks?' asked Royan.

'Well, they probably pushed some of them into the river to fix a dam in its position.'

'And why can't we see anything of the dam now?'

'Because Taita's people broke the dam themselves,' Nicholas said. 'Since then, the river has washed all the loose stones away. The Egyptians broke the dam to cover the entrance to the tomb.'

'They wouldn't have flooded the tomb itself, would they?' Royan asked anxiously.

'No. They only needed to cover the entrance. This quarry shows that a lot of building work went on here in ancient times. Only the Egyptians could have done this.'

'This was once a quarry,' said Nicholas.

'So, at last, I know that everything written on the scroll was true,' Royan said quietly. 'The quarry and the tomb of St Frumentius prove that there is a secret Egyptian tomb near this place – a tomb built for a Pharaoh.'

'Well, we know that Taita built his dam for a good reason,' said Nicholas. 'He changed the course of the river while he was building something else. Then he broke the dam to hide that something else. And we won't know what that something is until we build a dam ourselves and stop the flow of the river.'

'Oh, Nicholas, is that possible?' said Royan in surprise.

'With enough men and equipment, yes it is. We must go back to England to get the equipment. And we must find some good men who we can trust.'

Royan was silent for a moment. She looked around the quarry. The light was fading. The sun was sinking below the rock walls.

'How soon can we start?' she said. 'Let's go back to our camp now.'

'No, not tonight, Royan,' said Nicholas. 'It will be dark in half an hour and we can't clamber over all those rocks in the dark. We can sleep here. I can make a fire. The quarry is safe and dry and I have some food in my backpack.'

Royan did not like the idea, but she did not want to go back down the river in the dark. The two of them made a fire. They ate some food, then they lay on the ground beside the fire. They used their packs as pillows. Soon Royan fell asleep.

Nicholas slept too, but he woke before dawn. There was a lot of noise in the hills. He heard the distant sounds of guns firing several kilometres away.

'It's the sound of automatic weapons[36],' he thought to himself. 'Many people are shooting at something out there. We must return to camp quickly and then start on our journey to Addis Ababa immediately.'

35

6

Bad News

Royan and Nicholas got ready to move at dawn. As they were leaving the quarry, Nicholas saw something floating in the river. Fortunately Royan did not notice it. When he looked more closely, Nicholas saw that it was the body of a man. For a moment, the dead face of Boris Brusilov stared up at him, then it was gone on its way on the current down to the Nile.

Royan and Nicholas clambered back over the rocks and down by the waterfall and the pool. Royan had decided to call it Taita's Pool.

'What secrets are hidden here?' she asked herself. 'Well, we'll come back and find out.'

As they walked towards their camp, they saw a cloud of black smoke rising into the air. Even from a distance it was clear that something terrible had happened. And soon, they heard the voices of priests calling out prayers and crying.

Almost everyone in the expedition camp was dead. The men had been shot as they slept. The tents were burnt. Priests from the monastery were burying the dead bodies. The ground was covered with blood and flies.

Royan looked around the camp. She did not want to see the bodies. She was looking for her notes.

'My notes. Our films. All the records. They're gone,' she said.

'What happened?' Nicholas asked one of the priests.

'Soldiers came here in the night,' said the priest. 'We heard the sounds of guns firing. We heard screaming. Everyone was afraid.'

'Did anyone escape?' asked Nicholas.

'Only one man – Ali, the cook.' The priest pointed to a

man who was sitting at the edge of the camp. The cook was holding his hands to his head.

Nicholas spoke to him. 'Are you hurt, Ali?'

'No,' Ali answered. He did not look at Nicholas.

'Who did this?' Nicholas pointed at the ruins of the camp. 'What did they want?'

'Rebel soldiers did this,' said Ali. 'They wanted to find you. They shouted, "Where is the Englishman?" Then they shot everyone.'

'How did you escape?'

'I lay down. I didn't move. They thought that I was already dead.'

Nicholas looked at Royan. 'We must get back to Addis,' he said. 'We've lost everything here, but we still have the truck at the top of the cliff. It's a long walk, so we should start immediately.'

Royan nodded her head in agreement. She said nothing. She wanted to get away from the camp.

Nicholas and Royan said goodbye to the priests. 'We will come back,' Nicholas promised. Then they began to walk along the path up the cliff. They had nothing to carry except their backpacks, but soon Royan felt exhausted.

'How much further must we walk?' she asked.

'We can get to the top before sunset,' said Nicholas. He helped Royan up the path. It was a long climb. They reached the top of the cliff just as the sun sank.

'There's the truck,' said Royan. 'I didn't expect to see it again.'

'Yes, I can see it,' said Nicholas. 'And I can see something else.' He looked at the ground. 'Another truck has been here – a heavier one. There are marks on the ground. I wonder where it's gone?'

'Don't worry about that,' said Royan. 'Let's get in the truck and drive away, please, Nicholas.'

She walked towards the truck. Nicholas walked behind her. Suddenly he grabbed her arm.

'Nicholas! What are you doing?'

'Get back! Get down!' he shouted. He pulled her backwards and pushed her to the ground.

The next moment, the truck exploded. Nicholas covered Royan's head with his hands. Pieces of metal and rock flew in the air around them. The noise was deafening. They lay still and waited.

'Move very slowly and very quietly,' said Nicholas. 'We're going to get away from here, but we don't want anyone to notice us.'

'But, won't someone come?' asked Royan. 'The noise – the explosion – someone must have heard it. Won't someone come to find us?'

'Yes, but I'm afraid we won't want to meet them,' said Nicholas. 'Somebody was waiting for us. They put a bomb in the truck. I expect they'll come to check that we're dead.'

'How did you know?'

'I could smell the explosive as soon as we got near the truck. Somebody wants us dead, Royan.'

They crawled away along the cliff top. When they were far enough away from the truck, Nicholas stood up and led Royan away from the cliff. By now it was dark. They crossed a rough road and kept moving slowly until they reached some trees. They spent the night under the trees.

———

The next morning, Nicholas and Royan were still tired. They were also hungry and thirsty.

'What are we going to do?' asked Royan.

'We're going to walk,' said Nicholas. 'But we're going to keep away from the road. Somebody might be looking for us. If they are, we want to see them first!'

And so they began to walk. They walked all day. They

had nothing to eat. That night they stopped by a small stream and drank. Then they walked for a second day. They saw no one in the empty landscape.

'Let's go back to the monastery, Nicholas,' Royan said. 'At least we can get food and water there.'

'No. The monastery is the first place our enemies will look for us,' said Nicholas.

'Who are they?' asked Royan.

'Whoever is trying to kill us,' Nicholas replied.

'But *who* is it?'

'I don't know *who* they are, but I can guess what they want.'

'You mean that they want the secret of the Seventh Scroll,' said Royan.

'Yes. Someone took the scroll from your house in Cairo. They know about the tomb. They want to find it themselves.'

'But they don't know about Taita's Pool,' said Royan. 'I didn't make any notes about the pool. And I certainly didn't write down your idea about a dam.'

'I know that. But they *think* that they have enough information,' said Nicholas. 'They have all your notes and all our photographs. Somebody will be studying those very carefully. They don't need us any more.'

'What can we do?'

'We must get back to England. Then we must return here with men and equipment – and we must return soon. The level of the water in the river will be at its lowest next month. After that, the rainy season starts. We must find the tomb before the rains begin. The river will be twice as deep in the rainy season.'

'Your plan is impossible,' said Royan. 'We can't even get to Addis. We've no food or water. We're alone out here.'

'Well, I think we can take a risk and walk on the road now,' said Nicholas. 'We might find someone friendly. You never know. I've always been lucky.' He smiled happily.

They walked back to the road. It was getting dark. They saw the lights of vehicles in the distance. The lights were coming towards them.

'Hide!' said Nicholas. 'Let's see who's coming before we show ourselves.'

There was very little cover[37] beside the road. Royan lay down and tried to make herself as small as possible. The headlights came nearer and they heard the sound of engines. Nicholas lay beside Royan and watched.

'Four-wheel drives,' he said. 'I can see a line of three vehicles. There's a large man in the front four-wheel drive. It looks like – yes, it's Geoffrey!'

He jumped up and waved his arms. 'Geoffrey! I've always been lucky. This is my lucky day again.'

The truck slowed and stopped. Geoffrey Tenant from the British Embassy got out. Royan stood up.

'Geoffrey, we're very pleased to see you,' said Nicholas.

'I'm pleased to see you too,' said Geoffrey. 'We heard that you were dead.'

'That news was untrue,' said Nicholas, smiling.

An Ethiopian army officer got out of the second vehicle.

'This is Colonel Nogo,' said Geoffrey. 'He's interested in you too.'

'Nicholas Quenton-Harper,' said Colonel Nogo. 'I have received a report that you had meetings with rebel soldiers. You must leave this country immediately.'

'Don't worry,' Geoffrey said to Nicholas. 'I'll explain to the Ethiopian officials that you haven't done anything wrong. But I'm afraid that you two will have to leave the country. Colonel Nogo believes that you are friends of the rebel leader, Mek Nimmur.'

Geoffrey drove Nicholas and Royan to a small airfield near Lake Tana. They flew to Addis Ababa and stayed at

'You must leave this country immediately.'

Geoffrey's house. Royan felt better after a good meal and a bath.

_____

'Geoffrey, there are a few things that I don't understand,' Nicholas said the next day. 'Who told you that we were dead?'

'We received a radio message from a mining company,' said Geoffrey. 'The company is looking for minerals in the area near St Frumentius Monastery.'

'What's the name of the company?'

'Pegasus Mining.'

'Is it an American company?'

'The company is *managed* by an American, but it belongs to an Austrian. In fact, the Austrian gentleman is coming to visit us tomorrow. His name is von Schiller.'

'I've heard his name,' said Royan. 'My husband spoke about him. I believe Mr von Schiller collects Egyptian antiquities.'

'I'm sure that you would have a lot to talk to him about,' said Geoffrey. 'But you won't be able to meet him. You have to leave the country tomorrow. The British Embassy has issued new passports for you. They also asked for a renewal of your visas[38] to visit Ethiopia. Colonel Nogo refused.'

Geoffrey handed new passports to Nicholas and Royan. Inside the documents was a stamp from the Ethiopian Ministry of the Interior. It said: UNDESIRABLE ALIENS – NOT TO BE RE-ADMITTED.

'Is this bad?' asked Royan.

'Yes, it means that we have to leave Ethiopia. And we can never come back,' said Nicholas. 'But I still have an idea or two.'

_____

Geoffrey drove Royan and Nicholas to the airport the next morning. They were waiting to board the London flight when a private plane landed. A tall man in army uniform started to walk towards the plane.

'Look, there's Colonel Nogo,' said Geoffrey. 'He's come to meet someone who is on that private jet.'

Two men came down the ladder from the small private jet plane. One of them was tall and thin and he had thick black hair. Colonel Nogo shook his hand.

'That's probably the Austrian, Gotthold von Schiller,' said Geoffrey. 'Do you know him?'

'No,' said Royan quietly, 'but I know the other man.'

She looked at the second man who walked behind von Schiller. She knew this man very well. She had worked with him. He had visited her in hospital in Cairo.

'He's from Cairo,' she said. 'His name is Nahoot Gudabbi.'

7

Sapper Webb

Nicholas and Royan boarded the plane to London. Royan was silent. She was thinking about Nahoot Gudabbi. The last time that she had seen him was after the murder of her husband. Had Nahoot been involved in that murder?

Nicholas was also silent. He was making plans. And he was thinking about von Schiller. He was worried about the Austrian.

———

In Ethiopia, Gotthold von Schiller was worried about Nicholas and Royan too.

'What did they find?' he asked Colonel Nogo.

The colonel handed him some photographs.

'They took many pictures in the Monastery of St Frumentius,' he said.

Von Schiller looked at the pictures. 'This is a tomb, yes, but is it a royal tomb? I don't think so.' He gave the photographs to Nahoot Gudabbi. 'Read the hieroglyphics,' he said.

Nahoot Gudabbi looked through a magnifying glass. He studied the hieroglyphics in the photographs. 'These pictures were taken in a tomb, certainly. There is a stone pillar in the tomb and there is much writing on the pillar.'

'Yes, I can see that,' said von Schiller angrily. 'Tell me what the writing means. Tell me who is in the tomb. Give me a name.'

'The name on the stone is Tanus, Lord Harrab, the Great Lion of Egypt. He was a nobleman. He was a military general.'

'General Tanus – yes. Yes, we know his name from the Seventh Scroll,' said von Schiller. 'And here we have his tomb. But it is not the royal tomb of Pharaoh Mamose.'

'The objects in the tomb of Lord Tanus may give us clues,' said Nahoot Gudabbi. 'The royal tomb may be near the monastery.'

'Then I want to examine the contents of Tanus's tomb,' said von Schiller. 'Colonel Nogo, can you bring the objects here? The mining company will arrange the transport. I want you to take the objects from the monastery.'

'Yes, I can bring them,' said Nogo. 'There are only priests at the monastery. I can take everything. They can't stop me.'

'Good! Bring me the coffin of Lord Tanus and bring me the stone pillar with writing on it. I will be waiting for them.'

———

Nicholas and Royan landed at Heathrow Airport in London. They went to Nicholas's apartment near the city centre. Royan rested while Nicholas made several phone calls.

Nicholas called an engineer who lived in the south of England. The engineer's name was Sapper Webb.

'Sapper,' Nicholas said on the phone, 'I've got another job for you.'

'Bring me the coffin of Lord Tanus…'

'Yes, sir,' said Sapper. 'Are we going somewhere hot?'

'Yes, we are,' said Nicholas. 'Can you come to my London apartment tomorrow?'

'I'll be there by midday,' said Sapper Webb.

Nicholas's second phone call was to a bank in the Cayman Islands[39]. He gave a secret code number and arranged to transfer a quarter of a million pounds from his Cayman Islands account to a bank in the Channel Islands. 'That will give us some money to work with,' he said to himself.

His next two phone calls were more difficult. At last he got through to the number of the British Embassy in Addis Ababa and asked to speak to Geoffrey Tenant.

Geoffrey came on the line. Nicholas gave him a message for an officer in the Ethiopian Ministry of Defence. Geoffrey did not ask what it meant. He agreed to pass it on.

The reply to Nicholas's last call was a recorded message. 'This is the office of Africair Cargo Services. Please leave your name and number and a short message.'

Nicholas left this message, 'Jannie – this is Nicholas Quenton-Harper. Please call me at my London apartment. I've got a job for you.'

————

Colonel Nogo took two dozen men in two helicopters. They landed near the Monastery of St Frumentius. Nogo's men were armed with automatic weapons. They marched into the monastery and approached the tomb.

'Stop!' said the old abbot. 'This is a holy place. You cannot bring guns in here.'

'No one can stop us,' said Nogo. He pointed his gun at the abbot and shot the old man dead. The soldiers shot the guards outside the tomb. Then they broke down the wooden doors and dragged out the coffin and the heavy stone pillar. The priests tried to stop them. But the soldiers shot them all.

————

When Sapper Webb arrived at the London apartment, Nicholas showed him a map of the Dandera River. 'I made some quick measurements, here,' he said, pointing to the map. 'We believe that the Ancient Egyptians built a dam here. Now I want to build a dam here too. Can you do it?'

'Leave this with me for half an hour and I'll work out a plan,' Sapper replied.

'You'd better make a list of the equipment we'll need,' said Nicholas. Then he left Sapper to do his work.

———

Later that afternoon, Nicholas and Royan talked to Sapper about the dam.

'I can guess how the Egyptians built a dam,' said Sapper. 'They had plenty of stone from the mountains. They had some timber from the trees on the mountains. They also used something like bamboo or raffia or wicker[40] to make baskets. And they had a lot of slaves. Building a dam requires a lot of workers.'

'How did they build their dam?' asked Royan. 'And how will you build ours?'

'This is my guess,' said Sapper. 'The Egyptians started with two very large baskets – one on each side of the river. They made the baskets from plant stems. We call these baskets "gabions". They're very useful.'

'Do modern engineers still use gabions?' asked Royan.

'Yes, they do,' said Sapper, 'but today we use steel wire to make the baskets, not plants.'

'Go on, Sapper,' said Nicholas.

'OK,' said Sapper. 'This is what we'll do. We'll break tons of big rocks into smaller rocks and fill wire gabions with the rocks. Then we will build a bridge of gabions across the river. We will fill in the spaces between with more rocks. That's how to build a dam.'

'Won't the river wash these rocks away?' asked Royan.

47

'A lot of water runs down the Dandera River.'

'Yes, the river can wash away the rocks,' said Sapper. 'The gabions alone will hold the water back for a short time, but we have to work quickly. When we have a line of gabions across the river, we will put timber behind them and start to build a strong wall. The really difficult part is to get the central gabions into position and stop the river completely.'

'But the river will simply rise and flood over the top of the dam,' said Royan.

'It would do that if it had nowhere else to go,' Nicholas answered. 'We think that the Ancient Egyptians changed the course of the river along another channel.'

'I think that we need to raise the level of the river by less than a metre,' said Sapper. 'It will then flow down another channel – this one here.' He pointed to the map.

'I marked the channel on the map,' said Nicholas. 'Royan, do you remember when we looked down on the Dandera Valley? I said that the river had changed its course over the centuries.'

'But I thought that the channel was natural,' said Royan. 'Do you mean that the Ancient Egyptians put a dam across the river and changed its course?'

'Exactly!' said Nicholas. 'Taita the Slave built a dam. Then he built a tomb below the dam – or, at least, he built the *entrance* to the tomb below the dam.'

'So, he didn't work underwater.'

'No, he didn't do that. The river dried up after he built the dam. Then his workmen cut into the rock and built the tomb,' said Nicholas. 'After they'd finished building, they broke the dam and covered the entrance to the tomb with water. They didn't expect anyone to find it again.'

'How long did it take for them to do this?' asked Royan.

'To build the dam *and* the tomb? Maybe fifteen to twenty years,' said Sapper.

'Don't worry,' said Nicholas with a laugh. 'We only have to build a dam.'

'How long have *we* got?' asked Royan.

'How long will it take to build a dam? About two months, if we do it before the rains begin,' said Nicholas.

'The river is at its lowest level next month,' said Sapper. 'That's the time to build a dam. We don't have long, but I'm sure that we can hold back the river for a short time.'

'We'll be in trouble when the rains begin,' said Nicholas. 'Our dam won't survive the rains. The flood of water from the mountains will wash it away.'

'But all this work will need a large expedition,' said Royan. 'Why don't we organize a complete scientific expedition and build a dam next year?'

'First, no one will believe our ideas until we find the tomb,' said Nicholas. 'So we won't get money for an expedition. Second, we're not the only people looking for the tomb. Remember von Schiller. We don't want him to find it before us. He'll simply rob the tomb.'

'So, you're saying that we only have to *find* it,' said Royan. 'We don't have to excavate it and make a detailed study of it.'

'Exactly!' said Nicholas. 'When we prove that it's there, museums and scientific departments in universities all around the world will give us all the money we need. *Then* we will organize a bigger expedition and excavate the tomb. We'll go inside and study everything carefully. At the moment, we only have to find the tomb.'

'What if we're wrong? Perhaps there isn't a tomb below that waterfall on the Dandera River,' said Royan.

'You can't have doubts now, Royan,' said Nicholas. 'You *know* that it's there. You started to believe all this when you discovered Taita's scrolls. You've seen the tomb of Tanus. We know there's another tomb nearby – the tomb of Pharaoh Mamose.'

'Yes,' Royan agreed, 'you're right. But we can't go back to Ethiopia. We're "undesirable aliens".'

'We can't go straight to Addis Ababa,' said Nicholas, 'so we will have to get into Ethiopia another way.'

'How?' asked Royan.

'Leave it to me,' said Nicholas. 'I'm waiting for a phone call from Malta. Give me a few days to organize some equipment. Then we're going to take a boat to Valetta.'

8

The Return to Africa

Gotthold von Schiller and Nahoot Gudabbi were waiting in Addis Ababa for Colonel Nogo. As Nogo came into the Pegasus Mining warehouse, von Schiller stepped forward to meet him.

'Well? Have you done what I ordered?' the Austrian asked.

'Yes,' said Nogo. 'We have both the coffin and the stone pillar from the Monastery of St Frumentius.'

'Good. Bring them in. We'll examine them now,' said von Schiller.

Colonel Nogo ordered his men to bring the coffin and the stone pillar into the warehouse. The men carried them into the warehouse from a truck. Both the coffin and the pillar were very heavy.

Von Schiller pointed to the pillar. 'What does the writing say?' he asked Nahoot Gudabbi.

'This is the seal[41] of Lord Harrab,' said Nahoot. 'It tells us that the body in the coffin is the body of General Tanus. The slave Taita described the burial of Tanus in the Seventh Scroll.'

'Yes, yes,' said von Schiller impatiently. 'Now open the coffin. Examine the mummy, please.'

Nogo's men removed the lid of the coffin. There was a body inside. It was wrapped in long white strips of cloth. Nahoot Gudabbi began to remove the mummy cloths. He started at the head. The cloths were very old and came off easily. Then he stopped. Something shone brightly – something that was the colour of gold.

'Is it possible?' he said quietly.

Von Schiller looked into the coffin. He saw a gold crown on the head of the mummy. 'It is the crown of an Egyptian king,' he said. 'This is the mummy of the Pharaoh Mamose.'

'So, we have found the tomb of Mamose,' said Nahoot Gudabbi.

'No, you fool, we have not,' said von Schiller angrily. 'We've found the body of Mamose in the tomb of Lord Tanus. I expect that we'll find the body of Tanus in the tomb of Mamose.'

'And where shall we look for it?' asked Nahoot Gudabbi.

'I don't know. But I'm pleased that you're stupid,' said von Schiller. 'You and Nogo tried to kill Royan Al Simma. Because you're a fool, you failed. I'm pleased about that. I'm happy that she is alive. I expect that she and Quenton-Harper know where to look for the royal tomb. They'll find the tomb for us.'

'But they've gone – they've left the country,' said Nahoot. 'And they won't tell us what they know. Can we make them tell us?'

'We won't ask them,' said von Schiller. 'They'll show us when they return. We just have to wait.'

'Are you're sure that they'll come back?' asked Nogo.

'Oh, yes,' said von Schiller. 'They'll come back – not immediately, but they *will* come back. And you won't try to stop them until they've found the tomb, Colonel. Now, your

51

men must pack this mummy and its coffin into my plane. I shall fly to Austria at once. Tell me as soon as Quenton-Harper and the Egyptologist return to Ethiopia.'

———

When Nicholas and Royan arrived in Malta, Sapper was with them too. They drove a truck off a ship in the port of Valetta and travelled immediately to an old military airfield. They drove up to a black aircraft hangar[42]. Outside the hangar was a sign – AFRICAIR CARGO. Inside the hangar was a Hercules C-Mk1 plane. It was a huge aircraft that almost filled the hangar.

The plane's pilot was also huge. 'My name is Jannie,' he said to Royan in a loud voice. He was Dutch. 'I don't need to know what your cargo is, Nicholas, but I need to know its size and its weight and its destination.'

Nicholas took a paper out of his pocket and gave it to the pilot. 'I've got the details here,' he said. 'I didn't want to say much on the phone.'

Nicholas and Jannie talked for a quarter of an hour. Royan and Sapper drank coffee and looked at the plane.

'I guess that it's about forty years old,' said Sapper. 'But it's a strong plane. It'll take us where we want to go.'

'It certainly will,' said Jannie who was walking towards them. 'I've got extra fuel tanks. We'll need them. Nicholas has told me where you want to go.'

'What's the flying time, Jannie?' asked Nicholas.

'Well, if we flew in a straight line, I could get you there in less than twelve hours,' said Jannie. 'But we'll have to fly south first and then turn east. There are a few radar stations[43] that we have to avoid. I think that it'll take us fifteen hours.'

'You know the time for our meeting in the Sudan,' said Nicholas. 'That means we need to take off at around 04.00 hours tomorrow.'

'That's OK, ' said Jannie. 'Let's get this plane loaded.'

'My name is Jannie.'

Sapper opened the sides of the truck. Inside, there were many crates loaded onto pallets[44]. Jannie's son drove a fork lift truck[45] towards the pallets. He lifted each pallet and drove it into the cargo bay[46] of the plane.

'There's a lot of equipment,' said Nicholas. 'Jannie will have to make two trips. I've marked the pallets that must go first. We'll take the lighter equipment on our first trip. Jannie will drop the heavier equipment by parachute[47] on his second trip.'

'Where will we be on Jannie's second trip?' asked Royan.

'We'll be back at Taita's Pool,' said Nicholas. 'There's nowhere to land a plane near the Dandera River. We must set up a camp and be ready for the equipment to be dropped from the plane.'

———

Royan slept on a bed in the cargo bay. She woke up, briefly, when Jannie prepared for take-off. She heard the Hercules's engines roar and she felt the huge plane lift off the ground, then she slept until dawn.

When she woke again, she went to the front of the plane. She saw the grey-brown coast of Africa below them. The plane was flying south. Jannie spoke Arabic to an air-traffic controller[48] on his radio, then he turned the plane south-east. There was nothing to see except desert below them. It was a long flight.

Jannie did not speak again until later in the afternoon. He shouted above the noise of the engines, 'I can see the River Nile.'

They all looked out of the windows. A silver line on the ground stretched from north to south. It was the only water in the empty land. After they had crossed the Nile, Jannie turned the plane to the north-east.

Jannie flew the Hercules lower and lower. After another two hours, they saw a dark area on the ground ahead of them.

'Those are trees!' shouted Jannie. 'That means we're near the Blue Nile. There's not much daylight left. Look out for a large factory building.'

Nicholas and Royan could see nothing in the grey landscape, but Jannie's eyes were very good. 'There's an old Sudanese airfield down there,' he said, 'It's called Roseires. Look. There are landing lights. Someone is expecting us.'

There were small fires on the ground. Jannie took the plane lower and lower towards the signal fires. The wheels of the huge plane touched the ground. The Hercules rolled and bumped along the rough ground for several hundred metres. When it finally stopped, Jannie switched off the engines and looked out of the window.

Dark shapes approached the plane. Men came from behind the trees and bushes. They were all wearing camouflage uniforms and they carried guns.

Nicholas opened the side door of the plane. 'Mek!' he called out.

'Nicholas!' Mek Nimmur called back. 'Tessay is here. Where is Royan?'

Mek greeted Nicholas and Tessay greeted Royan.

'I have some bad news,' said Tessay. 'The Monastery of St Frumentius was attacked.'

'Tell us all about it,' said Nicholas.

But before they could say more, Jannie called to Mek. 'I have to fly back to Malta tonight. Can your men unload my plane?'

Mek had more than fifty men with him. It took four men to carry each of the pallets from the plane. They unloaded the cargo and Jannie got back into the Hercules.

'I'll be back in a week,' Jannie called down. 'I'll fly the rest of the cargo along the river and look for your signal. Be ready for the equipment to be dropped by parachute. Don't lose your radio transmitter.'

'I'll be in contact,' said Nicholas. 'We expect to return here in the middle of April. We'll be watching for you here on the fifteenth of the month.'

Jannie closed the plane's doors and got back into the pilot's seat. He started the engines, turned the plane and started back along the airfield. The Hercules was much lighter on its return journey and it took off easily.

9

The Dam

Nicholas and Royan listened to the sound of the Hercules's engines as the aircraft disappeared into the night. Then they turned to the equipment. Mek Nimmur's men were unpacking the cargo. From the cargo, they took some nylon nets and pairs of light metal poles. The men put many pieces of equipment in these nets and fixed them to the metal poles. They carried them with one end of each pole on a man's shoulder. Nicholas carried the most important piece of equipment himself – the radio.

'How far is it to the border?' he asked Mek.

'Two or three days' walk,' Mek replied. 'Then another two days from the border to the monastery.'

'Where are the soldiers who attacked the monastery?' Nicholas asked.

'We don't know exactly where they are,' said Mek, 'but we'll keep watching for them. We'll travel only at night until we reach the border. We'll be safer when we get to the river gorge[49].'

They walked along the river all night. At dawn, they stopped. The land beside the river was flat. There were no

56

hills before they reached the gorge two days later. The gorge was like a great wall of rock in front of them. The Nile came out of the gorge in a steady flow of water. The level of the river was very low. Nicholas was surprised. They could see sandbanks in the middle of the river.

'It doesn't look very deep,' said Royan. 'We could swim or even walk across it.'

'Yes. But in two months there will be a flood along this river,' said Mek. 'You won't think about walking or swimming in the Nile when it floods. You will see broken trees and even bodies floating in the river then.'

'Mek, what happened to Boris?' Nicholas asked.

'He followed us and I killed him,' said Mek simply.

'Yes, I saw his body in the river,' said Nicholas. He did not want to ask any more questions. Tessay was now living with Mek. She seemed happy.

They walked on for another two nights and they reached the monastery soon after dawn on the third day.

———

The Monastery of St Frumentius had a new abbot. He was a slightly younger man than the other abbot and he was friendly to Mek's rebel soldiers. He met the group of soldiers on the river bank below the monastery.

'St Frumentius brought our people the holy message from Byzantium many years ago,' said the abbot. 'Now his body is gone. It has been stolen from its tomb. But his message is still alive.'

'I have heard that St Frumentius didn't come alone from Byzantium,' said Nicholas. 'He had a brother, didn't he?'

'Yes, that's true,' the abbot replied. 'St Antony came with him.'

'And St Antony died before St Frumentius.'

'Yes, he did,' the abbot agreed, 'but we don't know where he was buried.'

'I bring you good news,' Nicholas continued. 'I have found an old map which shows the secret tomb of St Antony. That is why I have come here to the monastery.'

Suddenly, the abbot's eyes were very wide. He listened carefully as Nicholas and Mek Nimmur spoke about the tomb of St Antony. Nicholas explained that he needed workers to dig for the tomb.

'An aircraft will come with equipment,' he said. 'The equipment will help us to build and dig. But I need many men to help us find the tomb.'

'It is holy work,' agreed the abbot. 'We will help you.'

Mek Nimmur smiled and said to Nicholas, 'We'll have plenty of workers now.'

The abbot went to tell his people the good news. Mek led his men further along the river towards Taita's Pool.

'What did you promise the abbot?' asked Royan.

'A holy body – a relic – to replace the body of St Frumentius.'

Both Royan and Tessay were angry because Nicholas had lied to the abbot. But Mek disagreed with them.

'Pilgrims do not come here now to pray, because the holy relic of St Frumentius is gone,' Mek said. 'If we give the monks another relic, the pilgrims will come again. We'll give the priests the body in the hidden tomb. Then they'll be happy.'

Royan and Tessay were not pleased with this idea, but they knew that Nicholas needed many workers to find the tomb.

The travellers made a camp near the waterfall and Taita's Pool. Nicholas took Sapper to the site of the dam above the waterfall. Sapper made some measurements across the river.

'The narrowest point is twelve and a half metres wide,' he said. 'I can build a dam here. The river is only two or three metres deep at the moment. I expect its level will be twice as high when the river floods. A lot of water comes through here.'

He looked at the smooth rocks on the side of the river bank.

'The rains will start in a few weeks,' said Nicholas. 'The river will rise swiftly. We have to work quickly.'

'Get me as many men as possible,' said Sapper. 'We can start work as soon as the heavy equipment arrives.'

The next day, Nicholas marked out a drop zone[50] on the level area near the camp. Mek's men built several piles of rubbish around the area. The rubbish included all the plastic wrapping from the equipment they had carried.

'We'll set fire to the piles of rubbish,' said Nicholas. 'The plastic will burn and make a lot of smoke. Jannie will see our position from the sky.' He spent the rest of the day listening for Jannie's message on his radio transmitter.

It was late in the afternoon when a voice came from the radio.

'This is Big Dolly calling Pharaoh,' said Jannie's voice. 'Are you ready for the drop?'

'Look for the smoke of signal fires,' Nicholas said into his radio. 'We're ready for you.'

Mek's men set fire to the piles of rubbish. The rubbish burned and made clouds of black smoke.

Soon, they heard the sound of engines. The Hercules C-Mk1 appeared in the sky and circled above the drop zone. It flew round half a dozen times. Jannie's son was with him on this flight. The young man pushed big wooden crates out of the cargo door. The crates were attached to parachutes. The white parachutes opened and the cases floated down into the drop zone.

'The cargo has been received,' Nicholas said into the radio. 'Thank you. Expect us back at Roseires in the middle of April. Expect us on April the fifteenth.'

'I'll come for you on the fifteenth,' said Jannie. 'Good luck!'

The Hercules turned and started its return journey to Malta. On the ground, Mek's men dragged the crates towards the camp.

———

The next day, priests from the monastery brought many men to work on the dam. They did not understand what they were doing, but they expected to find the tomb of St Antony. The first job was to unpack all the equipment. Sapper put a diesel generator[51] by the river. This would make electricity for large powerful lights. He wanted groups of men to work through each day and each night.

Sapper's most important piece of equipment was a front-end loader truck[52]. The diesel fuel for the truck and the generator was in plastic barrels. There was enough fuel for several weeks.

Nicholas divided the men into groups of thirty. They put up tents so that they were living close to where they were working. Every day, women brought food from the monastery. Nicholas and Royan had their own cook – Ali, the man who had escaped when soldiers attacked their camp.

One group of workers broke rocks in the quarry. Three other groups carried the rocks to the river. Another group worked on the river bank where Nicholas had his camp. The men had to walk five kilometres to reach the opposite bank, crossing the river at a ford[53]. They carried broken rocks in baskets. They carried the baskets on their heads.

Sapper drilled holes in the rock of the river bank. Then he pushed long metal rods into the holes to mark the position of the first two gabions.

The gabions were huge baskets made of steel wire. The first two were lowered into the river when they were half full of broken rocks. Sapper used the front-end loader truck to carry the gabions. Then the men tipped more broken rocks and smaller stones from the quarry into the open tops of the gabions. Soon there was a mound of rocks above the water next to each bank of the river.

Next, Sapper put more gabions in the river. After four days, they had narrowed the river to half its normal width. Two walls came out from the banks in the shape of the letter V. But the centre – the point of the V – was not closed, there was still a gap. Now the river seemed to be calmer. The water flowed quickly through the gap in the dam and it was strong and silent until it reached the top of the waterfall. Then it poured into Taita's Pool with a crashing sound.

The level of the river was rising slowly. Nicholas told a group of workers to dig a channel further upstream. He wanted to change the river's course to another direction.

Upstream, one more group of workers cut down trees in the mountains. They made a raft[54] of tree trunks. The long timbers were tied together with thick wire.

Nicholas had brought some yellow inflatable boats[55] with the equipment.

'These inflatable boats are our transport to get home,' he said to Royan.

'You mean that we'll travel down the Blue Nile in those rubber boats?' asked Royan.

'Yes, we won't walk all the way to the airfield at Roseires,' Nicholas replied. 'We have six boats, but first we must use one of them to guide the raft. Groups of workers will also pull the raft into place from the banks, using ropes. I want to sink the raft in the middle of the dam and stop the river completely.'

'It's like the plug in a bath,' explained Sapper. 'I can't put any more gabions in the river at the moment. The water is too deep and it's flowing too fast in the centre. We have to hold the water back for a short time until we can get the last gabions into position.'

The men had built up a huge pile of stones on either side

of the river. They were ready for the most difficult part of the work.

Nicholas used one of the inflatable boats to push the wooden raft into the middle of the river. He wanted to guide the wooden raft into the centre of the dam.

Next, Sapper and some of his men used wire nets to fasten rocks to one end of the raft. When that end had sunk below the surface of the water, they tied ropes to both sides of the raft. Strong helpers pulled on the ropes from each side of the river. Nicholas and Sapper positioned the raft in the middle of the river, then they slowly guided the raft towards the dam. It was vertical in the water now and Sapper had to make sure that it fitted exactly across the V-shaped gap. The river was strong and raft moved more swiftly as it got closer to the gap. The water took hold of the raft and held it between the two arms of the dam. The gap was closed – at least for a short time.

As soon as the raft was in place, the water started rising. The timbers of the raft made a sound like a huge animal in pain. The river tried to push its way between the timbers.

'Quickly, now fill in the gaps with rocks!' Sapper shouted. Mek Nimmur translated his orders to the men.

Sapper ran along the arm of the dam to his truck. He lifted a gabion with his truck and carried it along the dam to the gap. He put more and more gabions into the water behind the raft. Men poured broken rocks into the wire baskets. Then they built a great stone wall behind the gabions. Lines of men worked swiftly for the rest of the day and all through the night. The rocks piled up. Spouts of water pushed through the wooden timbers of the raft, but it held the water back. At last, the stones were piled up all the way across the river.

———

'Quickly, now fill in the gaps with rocks!' Sapper shouted.

The men worked all the next day and all the next night. They poured stones onto both sides of the dam and built up sloping walls. The water level rose. Then, upstream of the dam, the river found another course. The water flowed down the channel which the men had dug. It flowed down the valley along an old riverbed and joined the main river again beyond the waterfall and Taita's Pool.

Nicholas looked at the dam. Was it high enough and strong enough to hold back so much water?

'Will it be OK?' he asked his friend.

'It'll be OK until the rains come,' Sapper replied.

They both looked up at the mountains. Great storm clouds were beginning to move over the mountain tops. It was the first sign of the spring rains.

'I think that the rains will come early this year,' said Nicholas. 'We don't have long. It's time to go downstream and begin work at Taita's Pool. Send some men with all the inflatable boats down to the monastery. We don't know when we'll have to leave this area, but it's a good idea to have them ready.'

10

The Entrance in the Pool

Royan was already beside the pool when Nicholas reached it. The water level had fallen. The pool was almost empty.

'Look, Nicholas!' she called out. She pointed to an opening in the wall at the bottom of the pool. 'Is that a cave?'

'That's an entrance to something,' said Nicholas. 'But it isn't natural. See how that rock has been cut! That's the work of stone masons. Let's get down there.'

They walked down into the pool. The water came up to

their knees. They looked into the opening in the rock. It was about a metre wide and two metres high.

'It's a doorway,' said Nicholas. 'It looks like the entrance to a tunnel, but the tunnel is blocked with stones.'

'The river has covered the entrance for thousands of years,' said Royan. 'Can we clear it? We must be very close to the royal tomb.'

'I'll get some men down here. We'll try to clear it. I expect the tunnel goes up into the cliff.'

———

The following night, two secret messages were sent and received by satellite radio[56].

The first message was sent from Africa to Austria.

FROM: PEGASUS MINING AFRICA
TO: G. VON SCHILLER, PEGASUS HEADQUARTERS

WE HAVE RECEIVED A REPORT FROM OUR SPY IN QUENTON-HARPER'S CAMP. THE DANDERA RIVER HAS BEEN DAMMED. QUENTON-HARPER IS EXCAVATING BELOW THE DAM. HIS CAMP IS GUARDED BY REBEL TROOPS.

The other message was sent from Austria to Africa.

FROM: GOTTHOLD VON SCHILLER
TO: COLONEL NOGO

MOVE TROOPS TO ST FRUMENTIUS MONASTERY. AVOID CONTACT WITH REBEL SOLDIERS AND DO NOTHING MORE UNTIL I ARRIVE.

The next day, Nicholas moved more men from the quarry to the pool. Although most of the water had drained from the pool, it was difficult to clear the tunnel. The men had to pull the stones away with their hands and only two men could work beside each other in the narrow space.

Sapper started the diesel generator and shone lights into the tunnel. Then the men could see what they were doing more easily. They worked on the larger rocks with metal bars and big, heavy hammers. At last, a large rock fell inwards into the tunnel. The workmen became excited.

Nicholas pushed his way to the end of the tunnel. Royan was behind him. Nicholas shone his torch into the hole at the end of the tunnel.

'There are steps,' he said. 'They go up into the cliff.'

Nicholas and Royan climbed through the hole. They soon saw that the steps led upwards into another tunnel. They moved carefully up the steps.

'The last person to walk on these steps was probably Taita the Slave,' said Royan. 'He was the last person to leave the tomb.'

They reached a large chamber and stood on a level floor. Opposite them was a doorway. The walls and ceiling of the chamber were smooth and dry. The doorway in front of them was sealed. Hieroglyphics were cut into the stone around the door. Royan translated them.

'The ruler of the Upper and Lower Kingdoms. The man who Osiris and Isis love. The friend of Horus. Mamose, King of Egypt. May he live forever in the other world.'

She turned to Nicholas. 'This is the Pharaoh's tomb,' she said. 'We've found it at last. Let's see what's inside it.'

———

An hour later, Sapper had brought his generator to the doorway of the tomb. He also brought tools to cut open the sealed door. Nicholas photographed everything before Sapper cut into the door.

The door was made of wood. Sapper cut round the edges and the door came away in one piece.

The three friends looked inside the doorway. Nicholas shone his torch along a corridor with a high ceiling.

'The colours!' Royan said. 'Look at the colours on the walls!'

The walls were covered with paintings. Nicholas and Royan walked into the corridor. It was like a picture gallery. The walls were covered with pictures of the Egyptian gods. As they walked along the corridor, they saw that the floor was made of polished stone. It reflected the lights of their torches and the colours of the walls and ceiling.

There were shrines[57] on either side of the tunnel. A statue of a god stood in each shrine – Osiris, Isis, Horus, Seth, Anubis and Hathor.

Nicholas stood in front of the statue of Anubis. The god had the head of a jackal and the body of a man. Anubis was the God of the Dead and the Lord of the Tombs.

'Mamose's burial chamber must be at the end of this tunnel,' said Royan.

They walked to the end of the tunnel and found another chamber. The walls were covered with more paintings. In the centre of the chamber stood a huge sarcophagus which was made from a single piece of stone.

The lid of the sarcophagus lay on the floor. Nicholas looked inside the sarcophagus. It was empty. 'The body of the king has gone,' he said. 'Someone must have broken in and taken it. But who? And how?'

―――

Over the following few days, Nicholas photographed everything that they had found and then packed the statues from the shrines into six wooden crates. Royan examined every corner of the tomb.

'Taita wrote about treasure,' said Royan. 'He wrote in the Seventh Scroll about all the treasure of Egypt. Where is it?'

'The seals of the tomb had not been broken,' said Nicholas. 'No one has been inside it for thousands of years.'

'Then there must be something more here,' said Royan. 'We haven't understood Taita's words correctly.'

'We don't have much more time,' said Nicholas. 'It's now

In the centre of the chamber stood a huge sarcophagus.

the end of March and the rains will begin very soon. Our dam won't hold together once the rains begin. Also I have to radio to Jannie to confirm our meeting. He expects us in the middle of April. I think that I should radio to him today.'

'So, we put our crates of statues into the inflatable boats, and we go down the river, back to Sudan?' said Royan. 'Is that your idea?'

'Yes,' said Nicholas. 'We've proved the existence of the tomb. We can ask for money from a museum or a university now. We'll come back with more men and equipment. We'll build a bigger and stronger dam and we'll explore this tomb thoroughly. But now it's time to go.'

'No, not yet,' said Royan. 'Please remember your promise to the abbot. We have to find the body of St Antony – or Tanus, or Mamose, or whoever was buried in this tomb.'

'But there is no body,' said Nicholas. 'You've seen that for yourself.'

'I have an idea,' said Royan. 'I remember something from Taita's writing about the tomb. "The Lord Osiris is the beginning." – that was how we translated what he wrote. I think that he was writing about the first shrine in the tunnel.'

'Yes, OK. The first shrine is at the beginning of the tunnel. Osiris is the first god. But do you mean something else?'

'Yes,' Royan replied 'It's possible to translate the text as, "The Lord Osiris is the opening." I think that we've seen what Taita wanted us to see – an empty tomb. The real tomb is still hidden and the secret entrance is probably behind the shrine of Osiris.'

'Let's see if you're right,' said Nicholas.

———

Gotthold von Schiller arrived at the office of Pegasus Mining Africa. Colonel Nogo and Nahoot Gudabbi were waiting for him.

'What is the latest information from Quenton-Harper's

camp?' von Schiller asked them.

'They've cleared and entered a tunnel at the bottom of an empty pool,' Nogo reported. 'They've removed several objects from the excavation and packed them into cases.'

'Have they found a mummified body?' von Schiller demanded.

'I don't know,' answered Nogo.

'Well, you must find out!' said von Schiller angrily. 'Or I'll go there myself and find out!'

'It is not safe to go there yet,' said Nogo. 'The camp is guarded by rebel soldiers. We must remove them first.'

'I'll come with you,' said von Schiller. 'This time there must be no mistakes.'

11

The Last Chance

Nicholas and Royan stood in front of the shrine of Osiris. They had removed the statue of the god and packed it into a wooden crate. Now they looked carefully at the paintings on the wall of the shrine. They touched the smooth surfaces of the paintings with their fingers.

Nicholas pointed to a picture of the sun. It was high up on the wall. 'That looks different from the rest of the painting. I can't reach it. I'll bring something to stand on.'

He brought two wooden crates. He put one crate on top of the other and stood on them. He looked carefully at the picture of the sun. 'There's an edge around it,' he said. 'I'm going to cut around the edge.'

He took a knife from his pocket and cut carefully around the picture of the sun. 'I think it will move,' he said. 'Can you help me to push it?'

Royan climbed onto the crates and stood beside him, unsteadily. Together they pushed at the picture of the sun. Slowly it moved backwards. It moved deeper into the wall. Suddenly, Royan lost her balance[58] and grabbed Nicholas's arm. They fell off the crates together.

At that moment, some stones fell out of the wall and landed on the wooden crates. The crates were crushed by the heavy stones. Nicholas and Royan were lucky. They were not injured.

Sapper heard the noise and he came running to the shrine. 'What happened?' he asked. He saw a cloud of dust. Nicholas and Royan were sitting on the floor. Broken rocks had fallen into the shrine of Osiris. Behind the rocks, Sapper saw a large hole.

Nicholas stood up. He shone his torch into the hole. There was a flight of steps beyond it.

'This is the entrance to the *real* tomb,' he said. He climbed over the rocks.

'Please be careful,' said Royan. 'There might be more surprises.'

'Then stay here,' said Nicholas. 'I'm going in.'

'You're not going in there on your own,' said Royan. 'I'm coming with you.'

They went slowly up the steep steps. After twenty steps they reached a level floor. They saw two doors, one on their left and one on their right. Ahead of them was another flight of steps.

'Which way shall we go?' Nicholas asked.

'Keep going up,' Royan answered. 'We can explore these other passages later.'

They went up to another level floor – a landing – and then to another. In all, there were six landings. Finally they reached a wall. Royan read the inscription on the wall.

71

'It says, "I follow the rhythms of the seasons. The earth promises a reward." And that's *all* it says,' said Royan.

'What does that mean?' Nicholas asked her.

'Let's think about it,' said Royan. 'But first, we should go back and tell Sapper what we've found.'

They went back to the shrine of Osiris. Sapper was waiting for them anxiously.

'Something is happening outside,' said Sapper. 'The men are trying to tell me something. We'd better go and look.'

Water was running into the tunnel. They splashed through it to reach Taita's Pool.

'Is the dam about to break?' asked Nicholas.

'Not yet,' said Sapper, 'It will break soon. We don't have the materials to make it strong enough. But the problem is up there.' He pointed upwards.

The water that was running into the tunnel did not come from the dam. It came from the sky. It was heavy tropical rain!

'How long have we got?' asked Nicholas.

'Only a few days,' said Sapper. 'We must leave before the river rises too high.'

'Yes, that's the answer,' said Royan suddenly.

'What?' asked Nicholas.

'The flight of steps and the landings from the shrine of Osiris represent the rise of the river,' said Royan. 'I think those steps were built as a trick. The first tunnel and the empty tomb were also a trick.'

'What do you mean?' asked Nicholas.

'I mean that Taita made these tunnels to trick any robber who broke into the tomb. We have only looked in tunnels that go up. Now I think we should look down.'

'Down from where?'

'From the shrine of Osiris.'

———

Soon, the workmen had cleared the broken stones and earth from the shrine of Osiris. They were very tired. They knew that the water was rising in the river and no one wanted to be trapped in the tomb. Nicholas promised them silver dollars in payment, but they were worried.

'The floor is cracked here,' said Sapper. 'We could take the stones up from the floor. We could see if there's anything underneath them.'

'I think that there's another passage under here,' said Royan. 'Let's take up the stones and look.'

The men pulled up the polished stones from the floor of the shrine. Underneath they found another layer of stone.

'How many layers do we need to cut through?' Nicholas asked himself.

'This layer is different,' said Sapper. 'It's a single piece of stone. It's like a lid or a cover. We'll try to lift it.'

The workmen put long metal bars under the edge of the huge stone. It moved. They forced the stone out of its position.

'You were right,' said Sapper. 'Look – there are more steps. And they lead *down*.'

This time Royan went first. She shone her torch onto a floor about twenty steps below. She walked down towards it.

As she reached the bottom, she began to feel dizzy[59].

'Nicholas!' she called out. Then she dropped her torch.

Nicholas took hold of her arms and pulled her back up the stairs. 'The air is bad down here,' he said. 'And we don't have any air tanks or breathing equipment. There's no fresh air in this place.'

'We have a large electric fan,' said Sapper. 'I'll connect it to the generator and I'll blow fresh air down the hole. We can go down again in half an hour.'

Sapper connected the fan to the generator and blew air down into the hole, while Nicholas and Royan waited impatiently.

While they were waiting, Mek Nimmur arrived with more

73

bad news. 'Government troops are coming this way,' he said. 'There is a group of soldiers by the river below the monastery. Another group is approaching the camp from upstream.'

'Can you keep them in these positions for an hour or two?' asked Nicholas. 'Our inflatable boats are ready near the monastery. We'll get out along the river. We'll meet you by the boats before sunset.'

'OK,' said Mek, and he left to give orders to his men.

Then Nicholas spoke to Royan. 'This is our last chance. We have about two hours. Then we'll have to leave, whether we find anything or not.'

'Right,' said Royan. 'Let's get down into this hole and see what we can find.'

———

This time the air was safe. Royan and Nicholas went down the stairs into the chamber. At the bottom they saw another flight of steps that led upwards. They climbed these steps and found that they were in a wide arcade[60]. On either side there were small chambers.

The chambers were filled with wonderful objects. There was ancient furniture – chairs and beds and chests. There were cups and dishes made of gold and silver. There were weapons and chariots. There were beautiful jewels.

The walls were decorated with pictures. There were paintings of gods and of the dead king, Mamose. The king was surrounded by the important officials who were members of his court. In the centre of one wall was the painting of an unusual face. The man in the picture had red hair and blue eyes. He smiled at Nicholas and Royan with a mysterious smile.

'That's Taita,' said Royan. 'I'm sure it's Taita. He looks different from everyone else. The painting is so good that he looks alive. His hair is dyed with henna – that's why it's red. But he's the only person in all the pictures who has blue eyes. Where did he come from?'

74

'He didn't know himself,' said Nicholas. 'Remember what he wrote. He was taken from his family and he became a slave when he was a very small child. He never knew his parents or his own country. We can only guess where Taita came from – Greece or Italy, perhaps, or somewhere further north.'

They passed in front of another picture. It was the picture of a queen.

'This must be Lostris, Queen of Egypt,' said Royan. 'Taita loved her. She was very beautiful. He built this tomb because *she* made a promise to King Mamose.'

'And where is the sarcophagus with the mummy of Mamose – or will the body of Tanus be inside?' Nicholas asked. They walked on and they looked at pictures and they looked into treasure chambers.

Beyond the treasury was another chamber with many shelves. On the shelves stood rows of *ushabti* figures – small statues like dolls. These figures represented all the workers of the royal court. There were priests and scribes, lawyers and doctors, gardeners and farmers, bakers and brewers, soldiers and barbers and hunters. They were the workers that the king took with him into the Afterlife. The spirits of the *ushabti* worked for the king and the other gods in the next world.

At last Nicholas and Royan came to the end of the arcade. The way was closed by a screen. It was a screen made of cloth. Once this veil had been the finest linen, but now it was old and rotted. It was as thin as a spider's web, and on it were glittering stars made of gold and silver.

'This is the veil of the royal burial chamber,' said Royan. 'Beyond the veil is the sepulchre[61] of the pharaoh. We have found the place at last. The body is buried here.'

———

Mek Nimmur and his men were in the quarry. Colonel Nogo's troops were moving along the river and Mek's men had been shooting at them for over an hour. The river path

'Beyond the veil is the sepulchre of the pharaoh. We have found the place at last.'

was narrow and Nogo's troops could only move forward two or three men at a time. The rebels had killed a dozen of Nogo's men. Their bodies floated in the river and the water turned red around them.

'Nogo's men are trying to circle around us,' Mek said to his men. 'Be ready to move back towards the dam and the monastery.'

At that moment, he saw a bright reflection from something metal on the hill opposite them. Then he saw small clouds of smoke. Seconds later, there was a whistling sound over their heads. 'Get down!' he shouted to his men.

They lay flat on the ground at the side of the quarry behind the larger blocks of stone. Mortar bombs[62] began to fall into the centre of the quarry. The bombs exploded with a deafening sound and sent fragments of stone flying in all directions.

'Nogo has sent men to the other side of the river,' said Mek. 'They can see us from the hills. If we stay here much longer, he may send aircraft to attack us. We'll have to move.'

At that moment, eight or ten men clambered over the edge of the quarry and began to move towards them. One of the men carried a big metal tube.

'It's a grenade launcher[63]!' shouted Mek. His men ran out from their positions. There was a lot of shooting and a lot of smoke. Mek ran towards the man with the launcher. The weapon was already on the man's shoulder. He was about to fire a grenade when Mek shot him. The other government soldiers hid behind rocks and fired their weapons wildly. Two of Mek's men were wounded and fell to the ground. More of Nogo's soldiers appeared at the edge of the quarry and started to fire down on the rebels.

'Go back!' shouted Mek to his men. 'Go back to the river. We'll fight them at the dam.'

His men dragged their wounded friends behind rocks and then began to move slowly towards the river. The rocks

77

protected them, but the rebels were outnumbered by Nogo's troops. It was time to get away.

12

In the Royal Sepulchre

Royan touched the veil of the sepulchre. The ancient linen fell into pieces as she touched it. On the other side, tall statues of the gods Isis and Osiris guarded a low doorway.

Nicholas and Royan walked through the doorway and into a small chamber. The room was just big enough to contain a stone sarcophagus. The lid of the sarcophagus was in its place. Robbers had not found this inner tomb. Perhaps this sarcophagus would not be empty.

On the lid of the sarcophagus lay a war bow. It was almost as long as Nicholas was tall. Shining, thin golden wire was wrapped round it.

'This is the bow called Lanata which Taita made for Tanus,' said Royan. 'It was Taita's special gift. Only Tanus was strong enough to pull its string. With that bow, he could shoot arrows further than any other Egyptian.'

At the foot of the sarcophagus, an *ushabti* figure stood on the floor of the tomb. It was the statue of a scribe.

Royan got down on her knees and examined the figure. She read the words that were inscribed on the base.

I am Taita. I am your friend. I will answer for you.

The words were Taita's promise to Tanus. He promised to tell the gods of all the good things that Tanus had done.

Two more of Mek's men died as they tried to leave the quarry. They were killed by fragments of stone when another mortar bomb exploded.

'They're dead,' said Mek to the man behind him. 'We can't help them. Get their ammunition. We need every bullet and every grenade. We must not waste them. And now we must get back to the dam.'

They clambered over the rocks beside the river. The way was narrow. Mek knew that Nogo's men would follow slowly and carefully.

'We can block the river path,' he said, 'but we can't hold Nogo's men in that position for long. They'll bring their mortars along the other side of the river. Move everyone slowly towards the monastery. I'll stay at the dam.'

———

Nicholas thought that he would need eight men to remove the lid of the sarcophagus. It was very heavy. Most of the workers had run away. But about a dozen workers remained near the tomb entrance with Sapper.

'Soldiers are shooting,' one man said. 'They have guns and bombs. They are near the dam. We must go.'

'A few mortar bombs have fallen on the dam,' said Sapper. 'I think that it will break soon. There's a lot of water coming down from the mountains and pushing against the dam, as well as enemy bombs falling on it.'

'We'll leave very soon,' said Nicholas, 'but we must take the body of St Antony with us.'

The workers remembered the holy relic. They pulled away the lid of the sarcophagus. Beneath it was a linen cloth covered with dried flowers.

Nicholas and Royan moved the cloth and they saw the golden death mask[64] of a king.

'But, look at the head,' said Royan. 'There is no crown. This isn't the mummy of a king. There are no royal symbols on the body. There is only the pharoah's death mask. This is the mummy of a nobleman, not a pharaoh.'

79

'Then this must be the body of General Tanus,' said Nicholas. 'That is why Taita left the war bow, Lanata, on the sarcophagus. The bow belonged to Tanus not to Mamose.'

'So Taita did put the body of Tanus in the tomb of Mamose,' said Royan. 'Everything that he wrote was true.'

'Yes, Tanus was the lover of Queen Lostris and the father of King Tamose. Tanus was a great man – as great as any pharaoh. He deserved to be buried in a king's tomb.'

The workmen got down on their knees beside the sarcophagus. Nicholas heard them say the words, 'Holy Antony – Holy Antony.'

'Holy Antony, yes, the monastery has a new saint,' said Nicholas. 'Let's take Tanus, or St Antony, down to the monastery where he should be.'

He helped the workers to remove the body and carry it out of the tomb. Nicholas took the death mask of the pharaoh. Royan took the *ushabti* figure of Taita.

———

Gotthold von Schiller arrived by helicopter. Colonel Nogo was speaking on the radio. 'We have forced the rebels away from the dam. It is safe for you to land.'

Von Schiller and Nahoot Gudabbi got out of the helicopter. Nogo did not join them immediately. First, he ordered his men to continue along the dry river bed. 'Follow the rebels,' he said. 'I will join you on the other side of the monastery. The rebels cannot escape this time. Kill them all.'

'I want to see the tomb now,' said von Schiller.

Nogo pointed to a man who was wearing a white robe.

'That is Ali, the cook,' he said. 'He was our spy in Quenton-Harper's camp. He will show you the tomb. Now I will go to finish this battle with the rebels.' He got into the helicopter and a minute later it took off.

Ali showed von Schiller and Nahoot Gudabbi the way to the entrance of the tomb. 'The Englishman removed very few things,' he said. 'They took a body to the monastery.'

'Colonel Nogo will get the artefacts later,' said von Schiller. 'Now, show us the tomb.'

Ali led them inside the entrance and up the steps that went to the chamber and the shrine of Osiris. They found the hole in the floor of Osiris's tomb and the steps leading down. Ali shone a torch. Von Schiller and Nahoot Gudabbi followed him down the steps and up the next flight.

When they came to the treasury and the royal arcade, von Schiller was amazed.

'Such beautiful objects!' he said. 'This is the greatest treasure that has ever been found. I shall build a museum to hold all these artefacts. It will be called the Gotthold von Schiller Museum. I will be famous.'

———

Nicholas and Royan reached the Monastery of St Frumentius. The workmen gave the mummy of Tanus to the abbot who was standing on the river bank.

'Holy Antony!' said the abbot. 'We have a sacred relic again.'

All the priests got down on their knees and prayed.

Mek Nimmur arrived with his men. Several of them were wounded. 'Nogo's men are coming along the river behind us,' he said. 'They aren't following us very closely – they think that we might turn and attack them. But we don't have long.' He explained the situation to the abbot quickly.

'There are deep caves behind the monastery which only the priests know about,' said the abbot. 'We will hide there. The soldiers will not find us and the relic of St Antony will be safe. We thank you for our holy relic.'

The abbot and the priests went into the monastery. They carried the body of St Antony carefully. They were not going to let soldiers take a holy relic away from them a second time.

'It's time for us to go,' said Nicholas. 'Put the objects from

'This is the greatest treasure that has ever been found.'

the tomb into crates. Are the inflatable boats ready?'

'All six of them are inflated and ready to go,' said Sapper.

'Good! Let's get down to the river now. Nogo's men are not far behind us.'

'I left a surprise for them at the dam,' said Mek. 'You said that the dam couldn't hold back the water much longer.'

They heard the sound of a distant explosion. The sound came from the direction of the dam.

———

The sound of the explosion reached the underground chamber where von Schiller was examining the treasure. He had his hands in a chest filled with golden objects.

'What was that?' he asked Nahoot Gudabbi and Ali.

All three of them listened. Then there was a soft movement in the air. It was like a distant wind.

'The dam!' Nahoot suddenly shouted in fear. 'The dam has broken!'

He and Ali ran through the tomb, towards the steps that led outside. Von Schiller was older and slower. 'Don't leave me!' he shouted out. 'Come back!'

Ali and Nahoot reached the tunnel near the entrance. Water was already flooding in, but they could walk through it. They had almost reached Taita's Pool and they could see daylight outside. Then suddenly a wall of water crashed into the opening of the tunnel and filled it to the roof. Ali and Nahoot were thrown against the rock wall and they were crushed.

By the time that von Schiller reached the first landing, the water in Taita's Pool had risen to its usual level. Water filled the first tunnel to the ceiling and there was no way out.

The lights began to go out and the generator stopped working. Von Schiller was alone in complete darkness.

Slowly, he went back to the royal burial chamber. He had to touch the walls to find his way. At last he went through the doorway guarded by Isis and Osiris. He found the sarcophagus and climbed inside it. Von Schiller lay down in the tomb where the body of Tanus had rested for so many centuries. Would help come? He knew that it would not come. The tomb was sealed with water. No one could enter or leave. And so he lay alone and in complete darkness, with all the golden treasures of Pharaoh Mamose around him.

13

On the River

Nicholas and Royan helped the last of the wounded rebels into the inflatable boats. Now all the men and all the crates were loaded. The Blue Nile had risen by three metres since the rains began. The river was flowing swiftly and the current was strong.

'These boats will get us back to the airfield a lot quicker than when we came,' said Nicholas.

'Have you got your radio?' Mek asked.

'Yes.' said Nicholas. The radio was in a strong metal case. He hung it over his shoulder.

'I'll lead the way down the river in the first boat,' said Mek.

'No, I'll go in the first boat,' said Nicholas. 'I'm the only person who's been on this river in an inflatable boat. I know the dangerous places.'

'That was twenty years ago, my friend.'

'It's still the same river.'

The men used paddles to steer the boats. The strong current moved the boats swiftly away from the monastery.

'Do you see any of Nogo's men?' Nicholas called to Mek.

'If they stayed on the river bed, they might have got wet!'

Mek shouted back. 'I hope that my little bomb gave them a surprise. They won't catch us easily now. We must worry about soldiers ahead of us, not soldiers behind us.'

The fast-flowing river was spraying water into the boats all the time. The men had to throw it out again with bowls and cups. A few kilometres further on, the line of boats raced down a series of rapids[65]. Although the boats were strongly made, the soft rubber might tear on the sharp rocks. It was also difficult to steer the boats, and all the men were exhausted after three hours on the river.

'We'll look for calm water!' shouted Nicholas. 'We need to find a safe place for the night. We can't steer in the dark.'

They found a place near the bank where the water was calm. The men were able to steer the boats to the bank and they fastened them to some trees.

'When will we reach the border?' asked Nicholas.

'If we continue at this speed, we'll be there tomorrow morning,' said Mek. 'Your cargo plane is due at Roseires the day after tomorrow, isn't it?'

'Yes, that's right. Do you want to come on the plane with us?'

'No, I have a war to fight,' said Mek. 'I want to find Colonel Nogo and kill him.'

'He might find you first,' said Nicholas. 'You've always been lucky, like me, but our luck is going to end one day. It will be safer to come on the plane with us. There's plenty of space. We don't have much cargo. We'll sell the statues from the tomb. They'll bring a good price.'

'Sell them and send me my share of the money,' said Mek. 'We need money to keep fighting.'

'Do you trust me, Mek?' Nicholas asked.

'Of course. We are friends,' the rebel leader replied.

'Friends are the easiest people to cheat,' said Nicholas. 'They don't expect it.'

85

The line of boats raced down a series of rapids.

Mek hit Nicholas softly on his shoulder and smiled. 'Go and sleep,' he said.

They slept on the hard ground. All of them were so tired that they fell asleep very quickly.

———

The next morning, they ate some cold food and then set off down the river again. The water was calmer as they got near the border and the mouth of the gorge. Suddenly Nicholas had a nasty surprise. He heard the sound of guns and the water in front of him jumped into the air where a line of bullets had hit it.

'AK47s[66]! Steer away from the bank!' Mek shouted.

Government soldiers were firing automatic weapons from the river bank.

Mek's men fired their guns at the river bank. But they could not see who to shoot at. The men on the bank were hidden behind bushes and trees. The rebel soldiers could only see the flash of guns firing.

'Keep shooting!' shouted Nicholas. 'We'll be past them soon.'

In only a minute, the river had taken them past the guns. But several men on the boats were wounded.

Soon it began to rain again and the boats were hidden from each other in a cloud of spray as the rain beat down on the river.

They heard the sound of a helicopter above them but they could not see it because of the low clouds in the sky.

'That must be Nogo,' Mek called. 'I expect he's taking men downstream to welcome us.'

'He may try to attack us when we stop for the night,' said Nicholas. 'But we've passed the worst of the rocks. The river is calmer from this point. I suggest that we keep travelling through the night.'

They tied the boats together with ropes and they travelled in a group. Soon they came out of the mouth of the gorge and here the river widened. The water was dark with mud but the current no longer pushed them along at high speed. The travellers relaxed a little, although they were all cold and wet and tired.

It was still raining when night fell. The boats kept on travelling through the night. They stayed in the middle of the river and the current kept them moving steadily.

'We won't see the airfield in the dark,' said Nicholas.

'Don't worry. There's a jetty[67] at the factory building beside the river,' said Mek. 'We can't miss it, if we steer along the left bank.'

They did not miss the jetty. They ran into it!

Nicholas grabbed one of the wooden poles of the jetty.

'Everyone get out here!' he shouted. 'We'll hide in the old factory and we'll hope to see Jannie's plane later. We need to hide these boats.'

They unloaded the boats and then deflated them. Sapper hid the boats under the jetty and covered them with grass and earth from the river bank.

'We ought to sink them to the bottom of the river, so that no one can see them from the air,' said Mek.

'We might need them again if Jannie's plane doesn't arrive,' said Nicholas. 'Leave them and let's get into the factory before daylight comes.'

The old factory had lost most of its roof, but they all managed to camp at one end of the ruined building. The rain had stopped, but they were all wet. They did not light a fire in case anyone saw the smoke in the dawn light.

———

The weather was clear the next morning. Nogo's helicopter flew low over the Blue Nile soon after dawn. He crossed the border and flew over Sudanese territory, although his pilot was worried about entering Sudanese airspace.

Nogo was angry and he did not care that they had crossed

the border. He had not expected Quenton-Harper to escape down the river during the night. He had sent men to the border, knowing that there were only a few crossing places. He had sent out patrols. One of his patrols had shot at six boats the day before. Where were those boats now?

Nogo was a long way over the border into Sudanese airspace when he told the pilot to turn back. They flew low over the old factory, which was the only building beside the river for a hundred kilometres. They could see nothing inside the building. Nogo looked for smoke or any other sign of a camp.

Then he saw something yellow. 'Land the helicopter by that jetty,' he ordered.

As soon as the helicopter landed, the six men in the back jumped out and stood with their guns raised. Nogo got out too and he looked under the jetty. The river had washed away some of the grass and earth that was covering the yellow inflatable boats.

'The Egyptians and the rebels are not far away,' said Nogo. 'And they will not be able to travel very quickly on foot. They must be expecting someone to meet them. You men stay here. I will come back with more troops and equipment.' He climbed back into the helicopter and took off.

14

The Escape

Nicholas watched Nogo's helicopter take off. 'We've got trouble,' he said. 'We need to move men out along the airfield. We need to keep Nogo back while our plane lands.'

'What shall we do if it doesn't arrive?' asked Sapper.

'Then you'll come with me back towards the border,' said Mek. 'We know this area better than Nogo and his men.'

Nicholas was listening to his radio. He heard nothing but crackling noises.

Nogo's helicopter returned with more men. Then it took off again. Nogo was building up the number of his soldiers by the jetty.

'He guesses that we're here,' said Nicholas. 'He'll attack the airfield first and then he'll surround us.'

Suddenly Jannie's voice came from the radio, 'Calling Pharaoh, this is Big Dolly.'

'Hello, Big Dolly, this is Pharaoh,' Nicholas replied. 'How far away are you?'

'About an hour and a half,' Jannie replied.

'Expect a difficult welcome,' said Nicholas. 'We've got people here that we didn't want to see.'

'I'll be ready for trouble,' said Jannie. 'I'll see you soon.'

Soon Nogo's helicopter returned with more men and equipment. These men were armed with grenade launchers and mortar bombs. They moved along the river bank towards the north end of the airfield. Mek's men moved along the airfield to attack them.

'Big Dolly, this is Pharaoh,' Nicholas said into the radio. 'Approach the airfield from the south. I repeat – approach from the south. The north end of the airfield is not safe.'

'I hear you, Pharaoh,' said Jannie. 'I'll approach from the south. What's your cargo?'

'Half a dozen wooden crates.'

'It was hardly worth coming all this way for half a dozen crates,' the pilot said with a laugh.

'Wait till you see what's in them. We may also have some wounded men. And you need to watch out for a helicopter. It's not friendly.'

'OK, Pharaoh, I'll be with you in five minutes.'

Five minutes seemed like a long time. The sound of automatic gunfire came from the north end of the airfield. Then there was the sound of mortar bombs exploding.

The sound of the Hercules's engines became louder than the sound of gunfire. The huge cargo plane approached the airfield from the south and lowered its wheels for landing. It touched down and the wheels threw up a cloud of brown dust as it raced along the airfield. Jannie slowed the plane immediately and turned it around at the south end of the airfield. He did not stop the engines.

As soon as he had turned, a mortar bomb exploded next to the runway. The explosion was only a hundred metres from the plane.

Jannie opened the cargo doors and shouted to Nicholas and Sapper. 'Get those crates onboard and we'll get out of here!'

Sapper and Nicholas pulled the crates to the plane and lifted them into the cargo hold. Nicholas pushed Royan into the hold after them.

'Get ready for a bumpy take off,' he said.

'What about Mek?' Royan asked.

'He's going to move his men back to a safer position as soon as we're in the air. He knows what he's doing. He can look after himself.'

The cargo doors closed. Jannie increased the speed of the

91

big aircraft's engines and turned the towards the north. 'A short take-off is what we need,' he said. 'Unfriendly people are coming towards us!'

Nicholas saw Nogo's men running towards them along the airfield. He saw the flashes from their guns as they fired at the Hercules.

'We're going to fly straight through them,' said Jannie. 'It'll take more than a few automatic rifles to stop this old bird. But keep your heads down in the back there. I hope that they don't manage to fire the grenade launchers. Those can do us some harm.'

The Hercules gathered speed[68] and raced down the airfield. A mortar bomb exploded at the end of the runway directly ahead of them. With a shout, Jannie pulled back on the plane's controls and the Hercules left the ground and climbed very slowly. He raised the wheels. The plane seemed to be only a few metres off the ground when they saw a helicopter coming towards them.

'I can't turn and I can't climb any quicker!' shouted Jannie. 'We must keep going straight and we must hope.'

The helicopter was so close to them now that Nicholas could see Nogo in one of the front seats. At the last moment, Nogo's pilot dived the helicopter under the cargo plane. Both aircraft were only about a hundred metres from the ground. The helicopter pilot lost control of his machine and it exploded into flames when it hit the ground a moment later.

Nogo's soldiers ran back towards the river when they saw that their leader was dead. Mek's men moved back towards the border, slowly, carrying their wounded men. The Hercules climbed away from the smoke of battle then turned west.

————

The helicopter pilot lost control of his machine.

Nicholas and Royan announced their discovery of Pharaoh Mamose's tomb when they reached Malta. They showed newspaper reporters the objects in the crates – the statues of the gods from the shrines. The statues were given to the Egyptian government and taken to the Egyptian Museum in Cairo by Royan.

The American Smithsonian Institute gave money to pay for a scientific excavation of the tomb on the Dandera River the next year. Nicholas Quenton-Harper was asked to lead the expedition.

Nicholas had one more thing to do before he returned to London. He needed to pay all the people who had helped him. He took a ship to Brindisi and then a train to the north of Italy. From there he crossed the border into Switzerland.

He had an appointment with a very rich American collector in Zurich. The American's name was Walsh. They met in a private room at the Bank Leu in Zurich.

Nicholas put an object on the table. It was the one arte-fact he had taken from the tomb himself – the golden death mask of Pharaoh Mamose. It shone in the light from the lamps in the room.

Mr Walsh looked like an old bird. He had small, bright eyes and a long nose. He had brought two men with him. One was a professor of Ancient History and the other was a well-known dealer in antiquities.

'I want to make sure that the mask is real,' said Mr Walsh looking at the death mask. 'I don't buy fakes.'

'And I don't sell them,' said Nicholas. 'Please examine the object carefully. It is real and it came out of a tomb only last month.'

'And where's the mummy that the mask came from?' asked Mr Walsh.

'I believe that the mummy is in the hands of Mr Gotthold von Schiller,' said Nicholas 'However, that gentleman has disappeared. We expect to find out more about him during the expedition to reopen the tomb. For now, no one else knows about the mummy or about the death mask. Are you interested in buying it?'

Mr Walsh looked at the professor and the dealer. The two men nodded their heads in agreement. Mr Walsh paid thirty million US dollars for the death mask. Nicholas sent half of the money to Mek Nimmur and Tessay. He kept the other half for himself and Royan. When he reached London, Nicholas paid Jannie and Sapper and all the people who had helped him find the tomb. Then he went back to Royan.

When the politics in Africa changed, Mek Nimmur joined the Ethiopian government. He became Minister of Defence.

Nicholas joined Royan in Cairo to make preparations for the second expedition to Ethiopia. Before leaving Egypt, they got married and they spent a week in Luxor on the Nile. They wanted to see the tomb of Queen Lostris – the tomb that was also the resting-place of Taita the Slave and the home of the Seventh Scroll.

POINTS
FOR
UNDERSTANDING

Points for Understanding

1

1 Why do Duraid and Royan Al Simma have the Seventh Scroll?
2 Who wrote the Seventh Scroll? When was it written? Why was it written?
3 Why can't Duraid and Royan continue with their work?

2

1 Who visits Royan while she is in hospital? What questions does he ask her?
2 What happens when Royan goes to her apartment in Cairo?
3 Royan mets Nicholas Quenton-Harper. What does she find out about him?
4 Do you think that Royan likes Nicholas? Do you think that Nicholas likes Royan? Give reasons.
5 What advice are Royan and Nicholas given in Addis Ababa? Who gives this advice?
6 What do Royan and Nicholas tell their guides at Lake Tana? What do their guides tell them?

3

1 'The tomb? What tomb?' asks Boris. What answer does Nicholas give? Why does he do this?
2 Where are the travellers when these words are spoken? What have they just seen?
3 Who do the travellers meet at the camp at the cliffs by the Dandera River? What do they learn about these people?
4 What thing does Nicholas see at the end of the meal in the church? Why is this important?

4

1 Who is 'the friend from the past'? Where do Tessay, Royan and Nicholas meet him? Why?
2 Where do Royan and Nicholas go during the evening festival of Timkat? What do they see?
3 There are two inscriptions in the inner tomb.
   (a) Where are they?
   (b) Who wrote them?
   (c) What do they mean?

5

1 Nicholas looks carefully at the banks of the river. What is he looking for?
2 Why doesn't he think that the Egyptians made the steps by the waterfall?
3 What do Royan and Nicholas find in an opening in the rock wall? Why do they think that this is important?
4 What do they decide to do?

6

1 Royan and Nicholas return to their camp. What has happened?
2 Nicholas and Royan leave the monastery. What happens when they reach the top of the cliffs at sunset?
3 Who says, 'You must leave this country immediately.' Why?
4 What does Geoffrey tell Nicholas and Royan in Addis Ababa?
5 Explain the problem that Nicholas and Royan have with their passports.
6 Who gets out of a private plane at Addis Ababa airport?

7

1 What objects does von Schiller ask Nogo to bring from the monastery?
2 Nicholas makes three phone calls from his apartment in London. Who does he call? What are the calls about?
3 How is Sapper Webb going to build a dam across the Dandera River? How is this similar to the dams that the Ancient Egyptians made?
4 What does Nicholas think about Taita's dam now?
5 Why must the expedition finish their dam in two months?

8

1 Whose body does von Schiller and Nahoot Gudabbi find in the coffin? Why do they think this?
2 Who do Nicholas, Royan and Sapper meet in Malta? How will this person help them?
3 When will the Hercules bring the rest of the cargo? What are the arrangements?
4 What will happen on 15th April?

9

1 Nicholas talks to the abbot about St Antony.
    (a) What story does Nicholas tell about him?
    (b) What does the abbot agree to do?
2 What is a 'drop zone'?
3 'Big Dolly calling Pharaoh.' Who uses these names? Why? What happens next?
4 What is Sapper's most important piece of equipment?
5 Why has Nicholas brought inflatable boats?
6 How are an inflatable boat and the raft used to build the dam?
7 What happens when the dam is finished?

10

1 What do Royan and Nicholas discover when they open the sealed tomb?
2 What is in the huge sarcophagus in the chamber at the end of the tunnel? Why is this strange?
3 Why does Royan now think that her first translation of Taita's writing is wrong?

11

1 Why does Sapper Webb run into the shrine?
2 '...the problem is up there.' Sapper points upwards. Why are Nicholas, Sapper and Royan worried?
3 'As she reached the bottom, she began to feel dizzy.'
   (a) Where is Royan?
   (b) What has happened?
   (c) Why?
4 Whose picture is in Osiris's tomb? Describe the painting.
5 What was in the chamber beyond the treasury?
6 Where is Mek? What is happening to him and his men?

12

1 It is: 'almost as long as Nicholas was tall, with shining thin golden wire wrapped around it'. What is this?
2 What is the meaning of the inscription on the base of the *ushabti* figure?
3 What is important about the golden death mask?
4 Where do the abbot and priests of the monastery take the holy relic?
5 What happens to Gotthold von Schiller?

13

1 Nicholas invites Mek to come with them in the cargo plane.
   What is his reply?
2 What does Sapper do with the boats when they reach Roseires?
3 Why does Nogo land his helicopter at the jetty ?

14

1 What happens to these people?
   (a) Nogo
   (b) Mek
   (c) Nicholas
   (d) Royan
   (e) Tessay
   (f) Jannie
   (g) Sapper
2 What happens to these things?
   (a) the *ushabti* figures
   (b) the golden death mask of Pharaoh Mamose
   (c) the mummy of Pharaoh Mamose

GLOSSARY

Glossary

1   **sequel** (page 4)
    a book or a film that continues a story with the same theme, or the same characters, from an earlier book or film.

2   **invaded** – *to be invaded* (page 4)
    when people from a country go into a second country and start a war, the second country has been *invaded*. The *invaders* usually take the land and the possessions of the people living there. This movement of people who start fighting is called an *invasion*.

3   **scrolls of papyrus** (page 4)
    the Ancient Egyptians often recorded important information, prayers and stories on *papyrus* – paper which is made from tall plants which grow along the edges of rivers and lakes. The Ancient Egyptians sometimes wrote their records on long, thin strips of paper called *scrolls*. The scrolls were rolled up and kept in stone jars.

4   **monuments** (page 6)
    large structures or buildings that are built for a special occasion or a special person. For example, the Egyptian Pyramids are ancient *monuments* made of stone.

5   **Department of Antiquities** (page 6)
    antiquities are very old things. Duraid and Royan work in a government department where they study Ancient Egyptian buildings and objects.

6   **hieroglyphics** (page 7)
    [haɪərəglɪfɪks] the Ancient Egyptians used small pictures – *hieroglyphics* – as their form of writing. Each of these pictures was the symbol for a meaning or a sound.

7   **slave** (page 7)
    someone who is not free because they are owned by another person. *Slaves* have to work for their owners, who give them food and somewhere to live but do not pay them.

8   **exiled** (page 7)
    when you have to leave your home and your land and can never return, you are *exiled*.

9   **satellite photographs** (page 8)
    satellites are instruments which travel high in space around the Earth. Cameras on the satellites can take photographs of the seas, rivers, land, cities and even buildings, thousands of miles below.

10 **monastery** (page 8)

a group of buildings where men live and pray and learn about religion. Holy men who learn about religion and teach people about a religion are *priests*. The leader of priests in a monastery is called an *abbot*. *St Frumentius* (*St* = saint) was the name of a holy man who lived in Ethiopia about 1670 years ago. He and his followers built a monastery in the mountains. The monastery was given his name. *Pilgrims* are people who travel long distances to pray in holy places.

11 **expedition** (page 10)

a journey made by a group of people who go to look for unusual places, people, creatures or things. *Expeditions* are often difficult or dangerous and might take a long time.

12 **hiring** – *to hire someone* (page 10)

pay someone to do some work. If you *hire something*, you pay to use something that belongs to someone else.

13 **black market** (page 10)

governments try to stop people buying and selling some kinds of goods or currencies. A *black market* is when people break the laws and buy and sell these things secretly.

14 **collector** (page 10)

Nicholas Quenton-Harper's great-grandfather visited many countries and bought many very old and beautiful objects. He was a *collector of antiquities*. He also sold these things. He was a *dealer in antiqities*. He particularly liked ancient objects from Egypt. He kept all these Egyptian artefacts together in a *collection* in a museum in his house.

15 **safety deposit box** (page 13)

a strong compartment in a bank where a customer's valuable items can be kept safely.

16 **notice of withdrawal** – *to expect notice of withdrawal* (page 13)

before customers take large amounts of their money or valuable items from their bank, they have to tell the bank that they want to do this. The number of days that must pass from when the customer tells the bank, to when the customer takes money or items away, is called *notice of withdrawal*.

17 **telephone directory** (page 13)

a reference book that gives the phone numbers and addresses of people and businesses.

18 **extension** (page 14)

extra rooms that are built onto a house, are called *an extension*.

19 **diplomats** (page 14)

officials who work for their own government in foreign countries.

20 **kilt** (page 14)

a short skirt which is made of material with many folds in it.

21 **bow** (page 14)

[baʊ] a weapon which shoots arrows. It is made from a long, thin strip of a strong material, usually wood. The bow is pulled into a curve by a string tied between its ends.

22 **risk** – *to take a risk* (page 17)

when you do something that is going to be very difficult or dangerous, you are *taking a risk*. You may be injured or you may lose your money when you do this thing.

23 **sheer drop** (page 19)

the path down the cliff is very narrow. On one side of the path there is a very high wall of rock, on the other side it is open – there is a *sheer drop*. The straight walls of the cliffs go down many hundreds of metres to the ground below. If their feet slip from the path, the travellers will fall a long way down and be killed.

24 **halted** (page 20)

stopped walking and stood still.

25 **chambers** (page 21)

small rooms.

26 **incense** (page 21)

incense is made from the seeds, stems and the dried juice of special plants. It has a strong smell when it burns. Incense is often burnt in churches or temples to show respect to the gods.

27 **camouflage uniforms** (page 25)

clothes which have large patches of green and brown colours on them. Soldiers wear *camouflage uniforms* so that they can hide easily among trees and rocks.

28 **upstream** (page 25)

the water in a river flows down towards lower ground and finally goes to the sea. When you travel *upstream* you are going towards the place where the river starts. When you travel *downstream* you are going with the river towards the lower ground. When the water in a river or the sea flows strongly in one direction, this is called a *current*.

29 **openly** (page 25)

Mek and Nicholas have been friends for a long time. But if the government knew that Mek – a rebel leader – had invited Nicholas to meet him *openly*, both he and Nicholas would be in danger. So Mek has ordered his soldiers to bring Nicholas to his camp secretly.

30 **Byzantium** (page 28)
almost 2000 years ago, the Romans ruled most of the ancient western world. For 400 years, the Roman rulers and their armies controlled all the countries around the Mediterranean Sea. They governed the lands and the people from Britain in the west, to India in the east, to North Africa and Egypt in the south and as far north as the Caspian Sea. All these lands were part of the Roman Empire. *Byzantium* was the Roman name for the city which is today called Istanbul.

31 **sarcophagus** (page 29)
[saːrkɒfəgəs] a large, decorated container for a dead body. It is made of carved stone, or gold, or some other material. In Ancient Egypt, the body of an important person was usually put in a *sarcophagus*. Often the body was contained in a painted wooden coffin, which was then put inside the sarcophagus. The bodies of important Egyptians were tightly wrapped in long pieces of cloth containing special oils and herbs. A body which was wrapped in this way did not rot and fall to pieces. It was called a *mummy*.

32 **diving equipment** (page 31)
people who want to swim deep under the water have to wear special *diving equipment*. Divers wear suits made of rubber, belts with heavy weights on them and they carry metal tanks of air on their backs. They breathe the air from the tanks through pipes that they hold in their mouths.

33 **swiftly** (page 31)
to move *swiftly* means to move very quickly. If a person or a thing moves very quickly, they, or it, can be described as *swift*.

34 **dam** (page 32)
a wall of stones, cement, wood etc. that is built across a river to hold back the water.

35 **clamber** (page 33)
climb up and over steep and rough rocks.

36 **automatic weapons** (page 35)
a rifle is a weapon that fires a single bullet each time someone pulls the trigger. An *automatic weapon* fires many bullets in a few seconds when someone pulls the trigger.

37 **cover** (page 40)
there were no rocks or trees to hide behind.

107

38 **visas** (page 42)

a *visa* is permission to enter a country or to leave it. The visa is stamped on your passport and checked by immigration officials. Visas can be used for a few months or a few years. If you want to visit the country after this time, you have to *renew your visa*.

39 **Cayman Islands** (page 46)

islands in the Caribbean Sea where you can keep money in a bank without paying tax on it. There are similar banks in the Channel Islands, which are to the south-west of Britain. Nicholas has made secret arrangements for money to be sent from his bank account in the Cayman Islands, to his bank account in the Channel Islands. He has *arranged for money to be transferred to* the Channel Islands.

40 **bamboo or raffia or wicker** (page 47)

bamboo is a tall plant with strong round stems. *Raffia* comes from palm trees. The stems and leaves are pulled into long thin strips. Willow trees grow by lakes and rivers. Their branches can be bent easily. When these thin branches are pushed together and dried they are called *wicker*. Bamboo, wicker and raffia are used to make baskets.

41 **seal** (page 50)

a symbol or mark which shows the name of a person. Important buildings, documents and artefacts might be marked with the *seal* of the person who owned them. If something is *sealed* it is closed up to stop anyone or anything opening it.

42 **aircraft hangar** (page 52)

a large building where planes are kept.

43 **radar stations** (page 52)

radar is an instrument that can show the movements of aircraft in the sky or ships on the sea. Radar finds the objects by using waves of sound. *Radar stations* are buildings where radar instruments are kept. Airports use radar so that officials know when aircraft are flying over their airspace, or territory.

44 **pallets** (page 54)

wooden platforms on which large and heavy loads of goods or objects are placed.

45 **fork lift truck** (page 54)

a vehicle that is used for moving large and heavy objects. There are two long metal *forks* at the front of the truck. The forks are pushed under a *wooden pallet* (see Glossary 44) and the heavy load is lifted up. The truck is then driven to the place where the pallet is unloaded.

46 *cargo bay* (page 54)

the goods and heavy objects that are taken from one country to another by plane are called *cargo*. The *cargo bay* is the area inside a plane where the cargo is kept during a flight.

47 *by parachute* – *drop by parachute* (page 54)

sometimes a plane cannot land because there is no runway. People, or objects in crates, can be dropped onto the ground from planes by *parachutes*. These are large umbrellas of thin, strong material that are attached to the person or object by cords. A few seconds after the person or object leaves the plane, the parachute opens and the person or object falls slowly to the ground.

48 *air-traffic controller* (page 54)

a person who is responsible for how and when planes take off and land at an airport is an *air-traffic controller*. Air-traffic controllers use *radar* (see Glossary 43) to watch the movement of planes in the sky over their airspace.

49 *gorge* (page 56)

a deep narrow valley which often has a river running through it. The *mouth* of a gorge is the opening at the beginning of a gorge.

50 *drop zone* (page 59)

a place where marks are put on the ground to show the pilot of a plane where things can be dropped by *parachute* (see Glossary 47).

51 *diesel generator* (page 60)

an engine that uses diesel fuel to make electrical power.

52 *front-end loader truck* (page 60)

a vehicle that can carry heavy things over rough ground. It has a wide box on the front that can be raised or lowered so that rocks, sand or equipment can be loaded in it. Front-end loaders are used for building or excavation work.

53 *ford* (page 60)

a place in a river where the water is shallow and you can cross it easily.

54 *raft* (page 61)

a platform made of pieces of wood that are fastened together. *Rafts* float on the water like boats. A long pole is used to steer the raft.

55 *inflatable boats* (page 61)

boats made from long tubes of rubber that are filled with air. The boats are light and can be easily lifted out of the water at the end of a journey.

56 **satellite radio** (page 65)
see *satellite* – Glossary 8. Satellites can also carry equipment that can receive and send messages by radio waves. A message can be sent from a radio transmitter up to a satellite that circles above the Earth. The same message can then be sent back to another place on the Earth, for a second person to receive on their radio transmitter.

57 **shrines** (page 67)
a small holy place where someone can pray to a god is a *shrine*.

58 **balance** – *lost her balance* (page 71)
the wall is moving forward and Royan cannot stand on her feet easily. She has *lost her balance* – one foot has slipped from the crate, and she falls.

59 **dizzy** – *to feel dizzy* (page 73)
when you *feel dizzy* your head feels strange and uncomfortable. You want to sit or lie down.

60 **arcade** (page 74)
a corridor which has many openings down both sides. The openings often have curved arches of bricks or stone.

61 **sepulchre** (page 75)
[sepəlkər] a tomb that is built of bricks or stone, or is made in a cave, or is cut into the rock of a mountain. The body of an important person is then placed inside the *sepulchre* and the entrance is closed up.

62 **mortar bombs** (page 77)
bombs that are fired many metres up into the air from long metal tubes that are placed on the ground.

63 **grenade launcher** (page 77)
a metal tube that is held on the shoulder of a soldier. A grenade – a small bomb that you can carry in your hand – is put into the tube and the launcher is fired. *Grenade launchers* can shoot grenades several metres into the air.

64 **death mask** (page 79)
a carving of a dead person's face which was put on their head in their coffin. Rich people in Ancient Egypt often had death masks made of gold and jewels.

65 **rapids** – *a series of rapids* (page 85)
a *rapid* is a place in a river where the water drops down a slope and moves more quickly. A *series of rapids* are many rapids together in one part of a river.

110

66 **AK47s** (page 87)
a type of automatic rifle. (See Glossary 36). The AK47 –
Automatic Kalashnikov 47 – was first designed and made in Russia
by a man named Mikhail Kalashnikov in 1947.
67 **jetty** (page 88)
a small wooden or concrete platform that is built out from the
bank of a river. Boats and ships can stop at *a jetty* to load or unload
their cargo or passengers.
68 **gathered speed** – *to gather speed* (page 92)
started slowly, then moved faster and faster.

A Guide to Pronunciation

Dr Duraid Al Simma	/ˌdɒktə ˌduəreɪd æl ˈsɪmə/
Dr Royan Al Simma	/ˌdɒktə ˌrɔɪʌn æl ˈsɪmə/
Nicholas Quenton-Harper	/ˌnɪkələs ˌkwentən ˈhɑːpə/
Nahoot Gudabbi	/ˌnɑːhuːt guˈdɑːbiː/
Mek Nimmur	/ˌmek nɪˈmʊr/
Geoffrey Tenant	/ˌdʒefri ˈtenənt/
Jannie	/ˈjæniː/
Colonel Nogo	/ˌkɜːnl ˈnəʊgəʊ/
Boris Brusilov	/ˌbɒrɪs bruˈsɪlɒf/
Woizero Tessay	/ˌwɔɪzərəʊ ˈteseɪ/
Gotthold Von Schiller	/ˌgɒtəʊlt fɒn ˈʃiːlə/
Pharaoh Mamose	/ˌfeərəʊ mɑːˈmɒhsiː/
Taita	/taˈɪtɑː/
Lostris	/lɒsˈtrɪs/
Tanus	/ˈtænuːs/
Seth	/set/
Osiris	/əʊˈsaɪərɪs/
Isis	/ˈaɪsɪs/

Published by Macmillan Heinemann ELT
Between Towns Road, Oxford OX4 3PP
Macmillan Heinemann ELT is an imprint of
Macmillan Publishers Limited
Companies and representatives throughout the world

Heinemann is a registered trademark of Harcourt Education, used under licence.

ISBN 1–405–07314–4
EAN 978–1–405073–14–1

This text is based on *The Seventh Scroll* © Wilbur Smith 1995
First published by Macmillan 1995

This retold version by Stephen Colbourn for Macmillan Readers
First published 2002
Text © Macmillan Publishers Limited 2002
Design and illustration © Macmillan Publishers Limited 2002

This edition first published 2005

Illustrated by Philip Bannister
Cover illustration by Chris Brown

Printed in Thailand

2009 2008 2007 2006 2005
10 9 8 7 6 5 4 3 2